HANDBOOK
on
ABORTION

by
Dr. & Mrs. J. C. Willke

Paperback

1st Edition . . . . May, 1971

2nd Printing, Revised . . . . August, 1971

3rd Printing . . . . September, 1971

HILTZ PUBLISHING CO.
Cincinnati, Ohio 45224
Phone (513) 681-7559

TABLE OF CONTENTS

Page

Foreword 1

Part I - Human Life?
1. Schizophrenic Society? 4
2. Is This Human Life? 6
3. When Does Human Life Begin? 9
4. Development in the Uterus 15
5. How Abortions Are Done 26

Part II - Price Tag: A New Ethic?
6. Rape - Incest 32
7. Mental Health 37
8. Unwanted Child - Right To Her Own Body 46
9. Population Explosion 52
10. How Many Mothers Die From Legal
    Abortions? 62
11. Physical Harm From Abortion? 68
12. Reduce Illegal Abortion? 74
13. Deformity of the Child 79
14. Religion, Values, History 87
15. Legal Rights of the Child 94
16. The Poor Suffer 104
17. What Doctors Think 107

Part III - Action
18. Correct Social Injustice 117
19. Family Planning 119
20. Birthright 122
21. Right to Life 128
22. The Words We Use 130
23. Insurance - Hospitals 132
24. Resources 134
25. Letters 136

FOREWORD

In the past several years, a tremendous push for more permissive abortion laws has occurred in the United States. With a few exceptions, the major newspapers and magazines of our country have participated in this movement by publicizing every new development and every argument, valid or not, in favor of liberalizing abortion laws. Those whose deep-felt convictions are pro-life have been labeled "anti" (abortion) and have been dismissed as traditional religionists and often, by inference, either Roman Catholic or influenced by that church's teaching.

Population explosion, illegal abortions and their fancied toll of maternal lives, the pitiable rape or incest victim, the deformed baby, the mother's physical or mental health -- these all in turn have been given top billing as reasons for change.

The movement has been sweeping away all who disagree. The pro-abortionists, who only two years ago were setting as their highest goal the incorporation in state laws of the controversial provisions of the American Law Institute's suggested changes, have now discarded that step-on-the-way and have been openly espousing nothing less than abortion-on-demand.

With little being said or written in the public press to counter this wave of propaganda, only a few private and religious publications, it seems, have attempted to present the other side.

The average citizen, when asked his opinion about abortion, will demonstrate an almost total lack of factual knowledge about the subject. He will tend to completely oppose "wide open" permissiveness, but will have a reason or two, stemming from the often false and misleading pro-abortion propaganda which has filled the public media, for which he feels abortion should probably be permitted. When pushed to define when human life begins, he usually will be even more indefinite. While only a very small minority of vocal people are aggressive proponents of abortion-on-demand, the great bulk of swing voters seem relatively apathetic.

To date, those committed to a pro-life philosophy have produced several excellent (and expensive) books and a rapidly increasing flow of pamphlets. The strength (and weakness) of most of the more modest efforts is that they are limited to only one aspect of the problem, are religiously sectarian, or try to cover too much too briefly. In an attempt to bridge this gap, we have written HANDBOOK ON ABORTION. Hopefully, it is small, concise, and inexpensive enough to be useful, without sacrificing too much detail.

Our emphasis, we are conviced, must be on the scientific, medical and social aspects of this issue if we hope to present the facts in a way that can influence our pluralistic society. Theological considerations are critical to each person individually but cannot be imposed upon other non-believers in the culture. This is not to minimize religious conviction. The value, dignity, and right to life of each individual which has been a hallmark of and lies at the core of western culture, is at least in part, directly related to our Judeo-Christian heritage.

Knowing full well that the anti-life side has been presented in its fullest by our public media, this book is an honest effort to present the pro-life side of the abortion issue. With this in his pocket or her purse may the legislator, doctor, clergyman, concerned layman, woman's activist, and all who value human life make their voices heard.

The hour is late.

PART I

HUMAN LIFE?

1

SCHIZOPHRENIC SOCIETY?

The following two items came to your authors' attention within the same week. The one, a confidential letter from the police department of a near-by city;

"Dear Doctor:

On Tuesday, November - -, 1970, a newborn baby was found in a cardboard box behind a supermarket in our city. Apparently, the baby was born sometime that day, and had been dead eight hours or more when found at 9:30 P.M. The autopsy showed the child had been stabbed seven times, suffered a head concussion, and was strangled with a zipper. In the box was the placenta and the severed umbilical cord. Obviously the baby was born without medical assistance. This may or may not indicate the mother has or will be seeking medical attention as a result thereof. The police request your assistance in locating this woman . . ."

The other, a newspaper article:

November, 1970

"An attempted abortion resulted in the live birth of one of a set of twin babies. Dr. Fritz Fuchs, chief of Obstetrics and Gynecology, New York Cornell Medical Center, explained after being questioned that the saline injection had been successful in killing one fetus but that unexpectedly a second, and live, twin had been delivered. Despite

4

all efforts to save the baby, it died after fifteen hours. Dr. Fuchs noted that in the case of twins it is sometimes impossible to inject the solution into both amniotic sacs."

Why is it that the police are only looking for the woman? What of the doctor?

Didn't the doctor clearly mean to kill both of the twins only one day prior to their birth? Since he succeeded in killing only one, and the other was expelled from his mother's uterus alive, why did he not kill this baby also when he found it yet alive? What magic occurred in his thinking once he saw the baby in daylight compared to when the child still lived in the darkness of his mother's uterus?

Why the total about-face from destruction of life to heroic intensive care attempts at preservation of life?

2

IS THIS HUMAN LIFE?

Is this human life? This is the question that must first be considered, pondered, discussed, and finally answered. It cannot be brushed aside or ignored. It must be faced and honestly met. Upon its answer hinges the entire abortion question, as all other considerations pale to insignificance when compared with it. In a sense nothing else really matters. If what is growing within the mother is not human life, is just a piece of meat, a glob of protoplasm, then it deserves no respect or consideration at all, and the only valid concern is the mother's physical and mental health, her social well-being, and at times even her convenience.

But if this growing being is a *human* being, then we are in an entirely different situation. If human, he or she must be granted the same dignity and protection of life, health, and well-being that our western civilization has always granted to every other human person. (See Legal Rights, Chapt. 15).

For two millenia in our western culture, written into our Constitution and Bill of Rights, specifically protected by our laws, and deeply imprinted into the hearts of all men has existed the absolute value of honoring and protecting the right of each person to live. This has been an inalienable, and unequivocal right. The only exceptions have been that of balancing a life for a life in certain situations or by due process of law.

6

--- Never in modern times, except by Hitler, has a nation put a price tag of economic or social usefulness on an individual human life as the price of its continued existence.

--- Never in modern times, except by Hitler, has a nation demanded a certain physical perfection as a condition necessary for the continuation of that life.

--- Never since the ancient law of paterfamilias in Rome, has a major nation granted to a father or mother total dominion over the life or death of their child.

--- Never has our nation legally allowed innocent humans to be deprived of life without due process of law.

Yet our newly enacted permissive abortion laws do all of the above. They represent a complete about-face, a total rejection of one of the core values of western man, and an acceptance of a new ethic in which life has only a relative value. No longer will every human have an absolute right to live simply because he exists. Man will now be allowed to exist only if he measures up to certain standards of independence, physical perfection, or utilitarian usefulness to others. This is a momentous change that strikes at the root of western civilization.

It makes no difference to vaguely assume that human life is more human post-born than pre-born. What is critical is to judge it to be, or not to be, human life. By a measure of "more" or "less" human, one can easily and logically justify infanticide and euthanasia. By the measure of economic and/or social usefulness, the ghastly atrocities of Hitlerian mass murders came to be. One cannot help but be reminded of the anguished comment of a condemned Nazi judge who said to an American judge after the Nuremburg trials: "I never knew it would come to this." The American judge answered simply: *"It came to this the first time you condemned an innocent life."*

Back to our basic question. Is this unborn being, growing within the mother, a human person? Make this judgment with the utmost care, scientific precision, and honesty. Upon it may hinge much of the basic freedom of man in the years to come.

--- Judge it to be a mass of cells, a piece of meat? Then vote for abortion-on-demand.

--- Judge it to be a human person? Then join us in fighting for his right to live, with all the energy and resources at your command.

3

WHEN DOES HUMAN LIFE BEGIN?

This is the question. Upon its answer all else depends. A mother who recently challenged the existing laws in Illinois was reported as saying: *"I don't think it's human. It's too small."*

Perhaps her opinion is as good as that of any other Mary or Joe we might meet on the street. Many would agree, many would disagree with her. Our only observation would be to ask the source of their knowledge upon which both pro and con would base their opinions.

Pro-abortionists have for several years been mounting a saturation campaign to effect drastic changes in our abortion laws and practices. Most of the average person's knowledge has come from a very one-sided presentation of facts, including a number of consistently repeated errors about abortion. It is no surprise that public opinion is slowly softening in its opposition to abortion. Few wish to be personally involved in this messy business, but the siren song of an easy solution seems increasingly acceptable for "others" to use.

But back to the question:

What is the opinion of natural scientists?

The most distinguished scientific meeting of the last decade that considered this question in depth was the First International Conference on Abortion, held in Washington, D.C., in October 1967. It brought together authorities from around the world in the fields of medicine, law, ethics, and the social sciences. They met together in a "think tank" for several days. The first major question considered by the medical group was, "When does human life begin?"

The medical group was composed of biochemists, professors of obstetrics and gynecology, geneticists, etc., and was represented proportionately as to academic discipline, race, and religion (e.g. 20% were Catholic). Their almost unanimous conclusion (19 to 1) was as follows:

> *"The majority of our group could find no point in time between the union of sperm and egg, or at least the blastocyst stage, and the birth of the infant at which point we could say that this was not a human life."* (Blastocyst stage is shortly after fertilization and would account for twinning.)

They continued:

> *"The changes occurring between implantation, a six-weeks embryo, a six months fetus, a one-week-old child, or a mature adult are merely stages of development and maturation."*

There has not been, before nor since, a more important or a more qualified body of natural scientists who, as a group, have thoroughly discussed and come to a conclusion on this subject. Until such time as some other group of equal scientific importance might possibly come to a differing conclusion, we believe that the abortion debate, from a scientific standpoint, must procede on the assumption that *this is human life.*

What was the basis for their scientific conclusion?

Modern science in the last decade has brought us a spectrum of knowledge about fertilization and early development that we had only guessed at previously in history. We now know that the sperm contributes 50% and that the egg contributes 50% of the new life. The sperm contains the genetic code of the father, and has no life or continuing function beyond the sole goal of its existence, that is, fertilization. The ovum contains the genetic code of the mother and is unquestionably part of her body. It has no other function than to be fertilized, and if it is not, it will die.

When, however, at fertilization, the 23 chromosomes from the sperm join 23 chromosomes from the ovum, a new being is created. Never before in the history of the world nor ever again will a being identical to this one exist. This is a unique being, containing within itself a genetic package, completely programmed for and actively moving toward adult human existence. It has, by any standard, a life of its own and in no way is part of the mother or the father. We call it a fertilized ovum and soon thereafter a zygote. Nothing will be added to this being between the moment of fertilization and its ultimate death as an old man except time, nutrition, and oxygen. It is all there in toto at that moment, merely not fully developed.

But how can it be human at that point? Doesn't it become human later?

Would we say that an adult has come from an infant? No, we would say that an adult once was an infant, but has since grown, matured, and developed into an adult. Everything the adult is was once contained in the infant, yet not fully developed.

In the same way, we do not say that the infant has come from the fetus or the embryo or the zygote or the fertilized ovum. Rather, we should say that the infant once was a fertilized ovum, or a zygote. He now merely is a more mature, larger, and more developed person than what he was, in entirety, at the moment of conception.

11

I've heard the fertilized ovum described as only a blueprint. What of this comparison?

The blueprint of your home is merely the plans for your home. After using this instruction sheet to build your house, you can throw the blueprint away. It has not become the house. The fertilized ovum, soon called a zygote, is not the blueprint but is in fact the house in minature. It itself will grow into the house in time. It is, in toto, the house already. Your home was built piece by piece and ultimately assumed a shape that could be identified as a house. The zygote, that was to develop into the adult person you are, was totally there from the moment of conception. All you needed to become the adult you are was nutrition, oxygen, and time.

The lady in the quote above said she didn't think it was human because it was too small. How can it be human when it doesn't look like a human?

If the only scientific instruments you use are your own unaided eyes, then a common judgment that you might make would be that it isn't human until it looks human.

We do have microscopes, electron microscopes, and genetic knowledge now that goes far beyond the limited knowledge obtained by your eyes alone. To base your opinion solely on what you see rather than upon what science is capable of telling you isn't very rational. This would apply whether determining if a patient has heart disease or if an unborn fetus is human.

Can't we consider the developing embryo a form of plant or animal life that only becomes human at some later stage of development?

Definitely not! The fertilized seed or ovum of a plant, of an animal, or of a human, upon the moment of fertilization and beginning growth, already is in totality that plant, that animal, or that human. Because of our present scientific knowledge of chromosome and gene structure, and of the intricate genetic programming that we are now aware of, we know that a plant can only develop into what it already is, that is, a plant. An animal, a dog for instance, can only develop into a dog, and a specific species of that dog. All of this is pre-determined and in totality already exists when fertilization occurs. The same is true of a human.

Why did the scientists say, "at least the blastocyst stage?"

The fertilized ovum is a single cell. Various names are given to subsequent stages of growth. The zygote stage implants in the wall of the uterus, after which we call it a blastocyst. The scientists mentioned this stage so that they could account for the fact that twinning and hydatidiform moles (a rare disease process) sometimes occur. Non-identical twins are two separate zygotes created by the union of two eggs and two sperm. Identical twins, however, occur when one fertilized ovum or zygote apparently splits into two, after which each of the two divided parts (each now a zygote in itself) grows independently in the very same manner toward full development and maturity as the average single zygote will do. This occurs sometime between fertilization and implantation in the wall of the uterus, but never after implantation.

Can we say then that one human person (zygote) can split into two human persons (identical twins)?

Scientific opinion is far from unanimous about how to consider this. One way of considering it is that the original human zygote, in splitting off a cell of itself or half of itself (whatever exactly happens, we don't know), can be considered in effect the parent of the new human zygote. This might be a form of parthenogenesis, or non-sexual reproduction. We know that this does occur in certain forms of plant and

13

animal life. We could postulate this type of process to explain identical twinning in a human.

What is crucial to identical twinning is that each of these zygotes is a human being with all of the potential of a human person, once this division and beginning growth has occurred.

But what if a person would sincerely doubt that this is human life in the womb?

Even if a person did doubt the presence of actual human life in the uterus at a particular time, what would be the fully human way to go? Perhaps a guide then would be how we have always treated other human life when there has been a doubt that it exists. Would we not resolve a doubt in favor of life? We do not bury those who are doubtfully dead. We would work frantically to help rescue entombed miners, a child lost in the mountains, or a person under a collapsed building. We would suggest that the truly human thing would be to give life the benefit of the doubt.

4

DEVELOPMENT IN THE UTERUS

Basic to the consideration of whether this life within the mother is human or even when this life becomes human must be the presently known scientific facts of the development within the uterus. Much has been learned in recent years. What are the facts? What do we know?

The sperm has life. The ovum has life. Why is either of these lives any different than when the two join and become a fertilized ovum?

Both the sperm and egg are alive, but in and of themselves have reached the fullest development of their potential. The sperm is part of the father, containing within itself the same genetic code as the father. The ovum is part of the mother, containing within itself her genetic code. Nutrition and time cannot add more to either of these cells alone, and in time both will die. Either alone cannot reproduce itself. When united together, however, they create a new being. This new being is totally different from either the sperm or the ovum, and from its mother or father, containing within itself its own complete genetic package programmed for active continuing development into a mature person. It may live or it may die at any stage of its development and later life, but it is a unique being.

Isn't the fertilized ovum only a potential human being?

No. It is not a potential human being. It is, rather, a human being with vast potential.

Isn't the fertilized ovum merely a blueprint of the human person that will later be born?

Definitely not. (See p. 12)

When and where does fertilization occur?

Sperm enter the mother's vagina, swim through the cavity of her uterus, out through her Fallopian tubes, and then surround her ovary. The egg, breaking out of the shell of her ovary, is penetrated by one of the sperm. This then becomes a fertilized ovum.

Wouldn't it be more accurate to say that each human person came from a fertilized ovum? This single cell is certainly not a human being, is it?

More accurately, you and I did not come from a fertilized ovum but each of us once was a fertilized ovum. To say that a mature adult comes from a child is hardly accurate. Rather, we would say that each one of us once was a child, and that as adults now we are more fully developed. Just so, the adult human person once was a child who was an infant who was a pre-born infant who was a fetus who was an embryo who was a zygote who was a fertilized ovum. Each in turn has become more fully developed and a more mature form of the human being who was there in totality at the moment of conception.

What happens after fertilization?

The fertilized ovum travels slowly back through the Fallopian tube and in approximately one week implants within the nutrient wall of the inside of the uterus.

How do you account for identical twins?

Identical twins apparently occur when a fertilized ovum splits into two identical separate fertilized ova, each of which then proceeds to develop into a full human person. (See p. 13)

How many weeks are there in a pregnancy and how do you measure them?

We measure a pregnancy from the time the ovum begins to grow, that is, at the start of a woman's menstrual period. After about two weeks of growth it is released from the ovary. The fertilization of the egg can then occur. This is two weeks before her next period is due. Four of the forty weeks have already elapsed at the time she misses her first period.

But the embryo is just a simple fish-like creature.

> *"The body of the unborn baby is more complex than ours. Before he is born, the baby has several extra parts to his body which he needs only so long as he lives inside his mother. He has his own space capsule, the amniotic sac. He has his own lifeline, the umbilical cord, and he has his own root system, the placenta. These all belong to the baby himself, not to his mother. They are all developed from his original cell."* (THE SECRET WORLD OF A BABY, Day & Liley, 1968, Random House.)

When does the unborn baby's heart begin to beat?

The heartbeat begins between the eighteenth to twenty-fifth day. (James M. Tanner, Gordon Rattray Taylor, and the Editors of Time-Life Books, GROWTH, New York, Life Science Library, 1965, P. 64.)

Electrocardiogram recordings can be taken at nine or ten weeks.

When does the brain begin functioning?

Electrical brain waves (electroencephalograph) have been recorded as early as forty-three days. (J. W.

Still, J. Washington Academy of Science, Vol. 59, 1969, p. 46.)

The brain itself is completely present by eight weeks.

When does the baby quicken?

"Quickening" is an ancient term usually referring to when the mother can feel the baby move. She usually will feel the baby kick at approximately twenty weeks (four-and-a-half months). This, however, is far too crude and inaccurate a measurement for today and civil laws that speak of "quickening" as detected by the mother are simply irrelevant and obsolete. Actual skeletal movements of the unborn baby begin at six weeks. (Hooker, Davenport, THE PRENATAL ORIGIN OF BEHAVIOR, Univ. of Kansas Press, 1952.) The mother cannot feel them then, however.

> *"In the sixth to seventh weeks . . . If the area of the lips is gently stroked, the child responds by bending the upper body to one side and making a quick backward motion with his arms. This is called a 'total pattern response' because it involves most of the body, rather than a local part."*
>
> Leslie B. Arey, DEVELOPMENTAL ANATOMY,
> 6th ed., Philadelphia, W.B. Sanders Co., 1954

At eight weeks, if we tickle the baby's nose, he will flex his head backwards away from the stimulus. (A. Hellegers, M.D., FETAL DEVELOPMENT, 31, Theological Studies, 3, 7 (1970), p. 26.)

At nine to ten weeks, he squints, swallows, moves his tongue, and if you stroke his palm will make a tight fist.

At eleven to twelve weeks, he is sucking his thumb vigorously. (Dr. A. Hellegers, above.) The most dramatic accounting of movement very early has been the following:

> *"Eleven years ago, while giving an anesthetic for a ruptured tubal pregnancy (at two months), I was handed what I believed to be the smallest human being ever seen. The embryo sac was intact and transparent. Within the sac was a tiny (one-third inch) human male swimming extremely vigorously in the amniotic fluid, while attached to the wall by the umbilical cord. This tiny human was perfectly developed with long, tapering fingers, feet and toes. It was almost transparent as regards the skin, and the delicate arteries and veins were prominent to the ends of the fingers.*

> *"The baby was extremely alive and swam about the sac approximately one time per second with a natural swimmers stroke. This tiny human did not look at all like the photos and drawings of 'embryos' which I have seen, nor did it look like the few embryos I have been able to observe since then, obviously because this one was alive.*

> *"When the sac was opened, the tiny human immediately lost its life and took on the appearance of what is accepted as the appearance of an embryo at this stage (blunt extremeties, etc.)."*

Paul E. Rockwell, M.D.
Director of Anesthesiology
Leonard Hospital, Troy, New York
Albany Times Union, March 10, 1970

When does he start to breathe?

By eleven to twelve weeks, he is breathing fluid steadily and continues so until birth. At birth, he will breath air. He does not drown by breathing fluid within his mother, because he obtains his oxygen from her umbilical cord. This does, however, develop the organs of respiration.   (LIFE BEFORE BIRTH, Life Magazine reprint, p. 13.) See 12 week fetus in amniotic sac – Fig. II, p. 20.

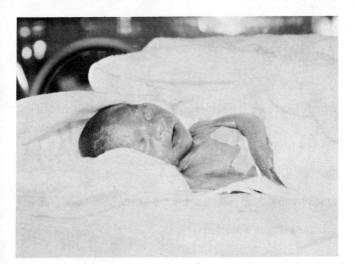

Fig. I Baby Kelly Thorman, born 3-30-71 at St. Vincent's Hospital, Toledo. She surprised her parents by coming prematurely at 21 weeks. In this picture, 3 days old, she weighs exactly one pound. (with permission of her parents)

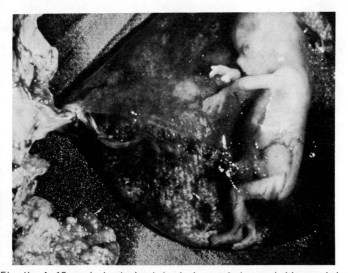

Fig. II A 12 week developing baby in its amniotic sac. (with permission, Wm. Hogan M.D., Rockville, Md.)

What of his stomach?

His stomach secretes gastric juice by eight weeks.

What of detailed development like fingernails and eyelashes?

Fingernails are present by eleven to twelve weeks; eyelashes by sixteen.

When would you say all his body systems are present?

By eight weeks.

At what point are all his body systems working?

By eleven weeks. (LIFE BEFORE BIRTH reprint.)

When is his brain working?

Electrical waves at six weeks certainly indicate function at that time. The movements mentioned above all require brain activity which is quite mature by twelve weeks. The famous Arnold Gesell has said, *"The organization of his psychosomatic self is well underway"* (at 12 weeks).

When does the mother feel the baby move?

Commonly by twenty weeks, which is a full fourteen weeks after he actually has begun to move.

How about teeth?

All twenty milk-teeth buds are present at six-and-a-half weeks. (LIFE BEFORE BIRTH reprint.)

Can a fetus cry?

"At eighteen weeks, equipped with a full set of vocal cords, it can go through the motions of crying but without air cannot make a sound." (LIFE BEFORE BIRTH, reprint, p. 16)

How does the size of the baby increase in weight?

At twelve weeks he weighs one ounce, at sixteen weeks six ounces, and at twenty weeks approximately one pound.

Why do so many legal documents speak of twenty weeks survival time?

This is again an obsolete concept which should be discarded. Dr. James Diamond has said that this *"twenty week survival time is about as sacred as the four-minute mile."* (AMERICA, July 19, 1969, P. 37) Some babies can survive today outside the uterus with modern care at or near this twenty-week time. Almost certainly, within the coming decade, with increasing sophistication of life support systems for babies, we will be saving babies that are born as early as twelve weeks, and possibly, with artificial placentas, much earlier than that.

See 21 week newborn child, Fig. I, p. 20.

Some state laws say abortion is legal until the baby is "viable." What does this mean?

Most people define viable as "capable of independent existence." We believe this is an extremely inaccurate word and should be stricken from the law books. By this definition, even a forty week, seven-and-a-half pound healthy baby after birth is not viable. Leave this healthy full-term child alone and he will die in a few days from neglect. He is not capable of independent existence, but depends totally on the life support given him by his mother.

When is a child capable of independent existence?

Certainly not before he's old enough to go to school. And we can make a pretty good case for him not being capable of it much before he's a teenager.

What does legal "viability" mean as far as legal rights of the unborn child are concerned?

Some states use "viability" as a measure of judgment as to whether or not the unborn child has the basic human right to protection of his life by the state. The frightening aspect of using this as a dimension of right to life is quickly apparent when we consider that, by this standard, a defective newborn child or a defective child of any age is also not "viable". By the above criteria, the senile old person rendered incompetent by a stroke, the completely psychotic individual, or even the quadraplegic veteran from Vietnam are all not "viable", as they are not capable of independent existence. Some of the above also do not have mental "viability." To make a judgment of an unborn child's right to live or not in our society by his mental or physical competence, rather than merely by the fact that he is human and alive, brings only too close the state's determination of a person's right to continued life as measured by their mental or physical competence or whatever the current price tag is.

What measure would you use instead of viability?

We would ask:

a) Is this being alive?

Yes. He has the characteristics of life. That is, he can reproduce his own cells and develop them into a specific pattern of maturity and function.

23

b) Is this being human?

Yes. This is a unique being, distinguishable totally from any other living organism, completely human in all of its characteristics, and can develop only into a fully mature human.

c) Is this being complete?

Yes. Nothing new will be added from the time of union of sperm and egg into a fertilized ovum until the death of the old man except growth and development of what is already there at the beginning. All he needs is time to develop and mature.

What is birth?

Birth is the emergence of the infant from the mother's womb, the severing of the umbilical cord, and the beginning of the child's existence physically detached from the mother's body. The only change that occurs at birth is a change in the external life support system of the child. The child is no different before birth than after, except that he has changed his method of feeding and obtaining oxygen. Before birth, nutrition and oxygen were obtained through the mother's umbilical cord. After birth, oxygen is obtained from his own lungs and nutrition through his own stomach, if he is mature enough to be nourished that way. If he is quite premature, nourishment would continue through our present reasonably sophisticated external life support systems in the form of intravenous feedings, which is similar to the umbilical cord feeding from the mother.

What of a cell from some part of a person's body that can be kept alive in a tissue culture, either separated from his living body or maintained after that person has died. Does this not upset the concept of the fertilized ovum as a human person?

No. Those cells were a part of a person and can only reproduce themselves as a specific type of cell.

The fertilized ovum is not a part of another person but is a whole person itself. It will not merely reproduce itself but is in totality a complete human being and will grow into a full adult if given time. Any one or hundreds or millions or billions of these cells in a human person's body can die and we do not say that the person has died. When a single fertilized ovum cell, however, dies, the entire person is dead.

The other important difference is that the fertilized ovum, subdividing and multiplying into many cells, moves immediately in the direction of specialized and differing parts, which are organized in a single unified complex being. Cells from parts of an adult human body in tissue culture can only reproduce their own kind and cannot go on to develop differing specialized parts.

5

HOW ABORTIONS
ARE DONE

There are four methods commonly used in performing an abortion. Nature has a fifth way, commonly called a miscarriage.

What is a miscarriage?

A miscarriage or "spontaneous abortion" happens when the uterus, for natural reasons, goes into labor and delivers a dead embryo or fetus.

Why does this happen?

We don't always know. Usually the growing baby has died because of abnormalities of itself or its placenta, and after this has occurred the mother has the miscarriage.

Is this dangerous?

Most miscarriages could quite safely occur at home. There is sometimes excessive bleeding, however, or incomplete emptying of the uterus and we often prefer to hospitalize the mother for observation or help if needed.

Is there any damage to the mother from a miscarriage?

Almost never. The cervix (womb opening) softens and opens itself and infection is rare.

What are the four kinds of induced abortion?

They are: 1) Dilitation and curettage (D & C), 2) Suction, 3) Hysterotomy, and 4) Saline poisoning. See Fig. III, IV, V, and VI, following p. 45.

What is a "D & C"?

To use this method the surgeon must first paralyze the cervix muscle ring (womb opening), then slowly stretch it open. This is difficult because it is hard or "green" and not ready to open. He then inserts an instrument, a curette, up into the uterus. With this he cuts the placenta and baby into pieces and scrapes them out into a basin. Bleeding is usually profuse. (Fig. III)

What is the suction method?

This is similar to a "D & C" except that a hollow plastic tube is inserted into the uterus instead of a curette. This is attached to a powerful suction apparatus. This tears the baby and placenta into small pieces which are then sucked out of the uterus and into a bottle. (Fig. IV)

The suction is the safest way, isn't it?

Many enthusiasts are loudly saying so, but all surgeons don't agree. Profuse hemorrhage is common in the first few days after this method is used. When this happens a second "D & C" with instruments must be done and often blood transfusions are needed. Shortly after New York began doing abortions in great numbers, these cases became quite common in most major midwestern hospitals. Four young ladies were removed from a single airplane at one stop because of hemorrhage.

How late in a pregnancy can a "D & C" or the suction method be used?

Most careful abortionists won't use these methods after the twelfth week.

What is a hysterotomy?

This is like a Caesarian section. The mother's abdomen is surgically opened, as is her uterus. The baby is then lifted out, and, with the placenta, discarded (see Fig. V). This method is used after the fourteenth to fifteenth week of development. One surgeon in our area who used this method removed a tiny baby who breathed, tried to cry, and was moving his arms and legs -- so he threw the placenta on top of the baby and smothered him.

You mean some babies are born alive this way?

Let's be specific. All babies are alive before being aborted. Abortion kills them. One baby in New York that was "aborted" in the above manner refused to die and has since been adopted into a good home. (U.P.I., Dec. 19, 1970)

What is the saline method?

This cannot be done much before the sixteenth week but can be used any time thereafter. A large needle is inserted through the abdominal wall of the mother and into the baby's bag of water. A concentrated salt solution is injected into this amniotic fluid. This immediately poisons the baby, causing him to convulse and die. About a day later the mother goes into labor and delivers a dead baby. (Fig. VI)

Are there any dangers to the mother from these last two methods?

The New York State Medical Society, in an official statement to its 22,000 members in 1970, warned that abortions done after the twelfth week of pregnancy are "fraught with tremendous danger."

A hysterotomy is comparable to a Ceasarian section in its problems. If the mother gets pregnant again, it will necessitate another Caesarian section to deliver her baby.

The "salinization" causes occasional brain and lung emboli (blood clots, etc.), resulting in the deaths of some mothers. One young lady seen by one of our colleagues suffered serious permanent brain damage from such an occurrence after getting off the plane from New York. (She, however, will not be listed as an abortion complication in the New York statistics.)

How large are the babies aborted at twenty or twenty-four weeks?

This is becoming one of the grisliest aspects of the entire question. (Fig. V & VI)

"Responsible" physicians would hope not to abort a mother whose baby would be over one pound. But -- one of our colleagues recently witnessed a four pound baby killed by the salt method and delivered stillborn. Another practice is that of some so-called physicians in New York City and elsewhere of injecting salt solution and immediately sending the mother home. Within two weeks in Cincinnati two babies weighing three-and-a-fourth and three-and-three-fourths pounds were delivered dead from mothers who had had this procedure. We find it hard not to call this, by any standard, deliberate murder.

> *Note:* *Your authors recently spoke in the Midwest to a diverse group of several hundred professional people. During the short intermission four physicians spontaneously came up to discuss six recent cases of significant post-abortion complications that they were treating. All six women had had a "safe and legal termination" in New York City.*

PART II

PRICE TAG:

A   NEW   ETHIC?

A NEW ETHIC?

But aren't we seeing a new ethic develop as to the value of human life?

Some are trying to say so. It might be interesting to quote a recent editorial (Sept., 1970) of the Journal of the California State Medical Association:

> *"The reverence of each and every human life has been a keystone of western medicine, and is the ethic which has caused physicians to try to preserve, protect, repair, prolong, and enhance every human life.*

> *"Since the old ethic has not yet been fully displaced, it has been necessary to separate the idea of abortion from the idea of killing which continues to be socially abhorrent. The result has been a curious avoidance of the scientific fact, which everyone really knows, that human life begins at conception, and is continuous, whether intra- or extra-uterine, until death. The very considerable semantic gymnastics which are required to rationalize abortion as anything but taking of human life would be ludicrous if they were not often put forth under socially impeccable auspices. It is suggested that this schizophrenic sort of subterfuge is necessary because, while a new ethic is being accepted, the old one has not yet been rejected."*

6

RAPE, INCEST

Picture the poor helpless girl, possibly your daughter, assualted by an unknown assailant, by inference possibly of another racial extraction, frightened, tearful, emotionally upset. Then a few weeks later, confirmation of her worst fears -- she's pregnant.

Who would be so heartless and so cruel as to refuse her an abortion? Why must this innocent girl be forced through the ordeal of pregnancy and childbirth? Talk is easy, as long as this is theoretical, but what if this were your daughter?

The above situation, charged as it is with emotionalism, pathos, and sympathy, has been sufficient to convince some state legislators to enact laws that permit abortion for rape or for incest. Is there anything more that can be said?

Is pregnancy from rape very common?

No. It is extremely rare.

Why is this so?

If a girl is raped or subjected to incestuous intercourse and reports the fact promptly, she is usually taken immediately for medical attention. This consists of a douche, commonly a scraping of the uterus, and at times doses of medication, one or all of which, while done partially to prevent venereal disease, will also almost invariably prevent her from getting pregnant. If the rape victim would report her assualt promptly, there would be, for all practical purposes, no pregnancies from rape.

Do most young women know this?

If they don't, they certainly should.

Are there any statistics to support the fact that pregnancy is rare?

There have been few good statistical studies in this country. In Czechoslovakia, however, out of 86,000 consecutive induced abortions, only twenty-two were done for rape. This figures out to one in 4,000. At a recent obstetric meeting at a major midwest hospital, a poll taken of those physicians present (who had delivered over 19,000 babies) revealed that not one had delivered a bona fide rape pregnancy.

What has been the English experience?

English law does not even list rape as a reason for abortion, because of "the difficulty of proving rape."

What is meant by "difficulty of proving rape"?

This is the crux of the problem and it goes something like this: Let's assume a young woman is raped, but that through fright or ignorance she does not report it and quietly nurses her fears. She misses her period and hopes against hope that it isn't what she thinks it is. Another week, yet another week, and finally in tears she reports to her mother, her physician, or some other counselor or confidante.

Let's assume that the law permits abortion for rape and that her parents bring her to the District Attorney and request that this be performed. The representative of the law may be quite sympathetic and more than willing to help her, but he has one request that must be met: "Since this is a law, and I must have reasonable proof that you were raped, you must furnish me with one reliable witness to corroborate your story." This she cannot do. Therefore, he cannot authorize the abortion for this reason.

But think of the poor girl.

True, if in fact she was actually raped against her will. As everyone knows, there are many degrees of resistance or consent on the part of a woman to the act of intercourse. It is easy for a woman rejected by a lover to then accuse him of raping her. For any kind of justice, some type of proof must be asked.

What of incest?

Incest is intercourse by a father with his daughter, uncle with niece, etc. The same dynamics mentioned above apply. Will Uncle John admit to having relations with his niece? Never! It would be her word against his. The court might even believe her, but could not act on it legally. Incestuous intercourse is seldom reported and when pregnancy does occur, it is not usually reported as being from incest.

What of a law for rape or incest then?

We would call them non-laws, as they would be almost totally inoperative. We believe that rape and incest as reasons for liberalizing abortion laws are little but an emotional smoke screen behind which to open the door for permissive abortion for many other reasons.

But, even if rare, some girls are forcefully raped and some do get pregnant. Should they be forced to carry an unwanted child?

Legal authorities say that to change the entire law for a very few cases would possibly open a Pandora's Box.

But think of the poor girl -- the trauma to her!

Unquestionably, many would want her to destroy the growing baby within her. But before making this decision, remember that most of the trauma has already occurred. She has been raped. That trauma will live with her all of her life. Furthermore, this girl did not report for help but kept this to herself. For several weeks she thought of little else as the panic built up. Now she has finally asked for help, has shared her upset, and should be in a supportive situation.

The utilitarian question from the mother's standpoint is whether or not it would now be better to kill the developing baby within her. But will abortion now be best for her, or will it bring her more harm yet? What has happened and its damage has already occurred. She's old enough to know and have an opinion as to whether she carries a "baby" or a "blob of protoplasm."

Will she be able to live comfortably with the memory that she killed her developing baby? Or would she ultimately be more mature and more at peace with herself if she could remember that, even though she was unwillingly pregnant, she nevertheless gave her child life and a good home (perhaps through adoption).

Even from only the mother's standpoint, the choice is one which deserves the most serious deliberation, and no answer is easy or automatically right.

and finally:

Isn't it a twisted logic

that would kill an innocent

unborn baby for the crime

of his father!

7

MENTAL HEALTH

"Maternal mental health was the commonest indications for hospital abortion in 1969, accounting for 93.7% of all cases."

Abortion Survelliance Report,
Annual Summary
U.S. Dept. of Health, Education & Welfare

How new is mental health as an indication for abortion?

It is quite new and has been spoken of only in the last few years. Since the decline and virtual disappearance of therapeutic abortion of the type that once was necessary to save the life of the mother, many major university hospitals have gone a decade or more without doing a single therapeutic abortion. For instance, the University Hospital of the College of Medicine at the University of Cincinnati did not do a single therapeutic abortion for fifteen years prior to 1968. This experience is not unusual. (W. Stone, Dept. of Psychiatry, U. of C., Feb, 1971.)

Already in 1951, Dr. R.J. Hefferman, of Tufts University, speaking to the Congress of the American College of Surgeons, said: *"Anyone who performs a therapeutic abortion (for physical disease) is either ignorant of modern methods of treating the complications of pregnancy, or is unwilling to take time to use them."*

So abortion is rarely necessary today to save a mother's life?

Yes, abortion is almost never necessary anymore.

But isn't it sometimes necessary to preserve her mental health?

The word "mental health" is so broad and vague as to be almost meaningless. In fact, in the last few years, it has become a catch-all reason for which all sorts of abortions have been justified, only rarely in fact being done for serious psychiatric reasons.

What would be a serious psychiatric reason?

Frank Ayd, M.D., medical editor and nationally known psychiatrist has said: *"True psychiatric reasons for abortion have become practically non-existent. Modern psychiatric therapy has made it possible to carry a mentally ill woman to term."*

It can be flatly stated that no mental disease known to man can be cured by abortion. The most that can be said is that possible mental breakdowns or complications might be prevented by abortion. To predict this accurately, however, is quite frankly beyond the competence of ordinary men, and we include psychiatrists in this group. There are so many variables, people are so different, and react in so many different ways, that no one, no matter what his training, can accurately predict what effect a pregnancy or an abortion will have on a woman.

That's one opinion. Can you cite other authorities?

Dr. Theodore Litz, Yale University Psychiatrist,

has said: *"It is practically impossible to predict when an abortion will not be more detrimental to the mental health of the mother than carrying her child to birth."*

Dr. R. Bruce Sloan of Temple University (who would permit abortions), writing in the New England Journal of Medicine, May 29, 1969, said: ' *"There are no unequivocable psychiatric indications for abortion."* He stated further that if the pregnancy is not interrupted, *"The risk of flare-up or precipitation of psychosis is small and unpredictable, and suicide is rare."*

Suicide is rare? I thought it was common in women who were refused abortion.

This is an oft-repeated fallacy. Suicide among pregnant women is extremely rare. Several well-controlled studies have shown conclusively that the actual incidence of suicide among pregnant women is less than one-fourth that of the general female population of the same age. (See p. 45 Minnesota).

That's hard to believe.

A good example comes from Sweden. In a series of 344 women who were refused legal abortion in Sweden for a variety of reasons, 62 specifically stated that they would commit suicide. It was determined that none of them did. (ABORTION AND PSYCHIATRY, Richard Vaughan, Dept. of Psychology, Univ. of San Francisco.)

But does Sweden's experience compare to that of the United States?

It would certainly be comparable to the experience of many of our states or large cities. Perhaps a good comparison would be to compare Sweden with Minnesota. Both have relatively similar population groups; both have generally excellent medical care.

But some pregnant women do commit suicide, don't they?

Minnesota is the source of some of the figures on maternal suicides. Their suicides of pregnant women have averaged about one per year. It is interesting to note that almost three-fourths of these have occurred in women who have not seen a psychiatrist. As Dr. Frank Ayd mentioned in the question above, when women are under competent psychiatric care, they can be adequately supported through their pregnancies. Abortion for "mental health" is in some areas frequently approved by psychiatrists, which adds one more paradox to the confusing abortion scene in this country.

What occurs at times today is that the psychiatrist, who should be capable of helping the woman through her pregnancy by virtue of his skill, may advise an abortion. This doesn't cure the psychiatric illness, being at best only symptomatic treatment. Most commonly, after such an encounter, there is no follow-up psychiatric treatment. To most inquiring minds, this would seem to confirm the fact that there was no major mental illness in the first place.

Are you saying that mental illness is usually just an excuse for an abortion?

We are saying exactly that.

But don't several physicians usually have to certify that there is mental illness?

In practice, the need for certification by several physicians (psychiatrists or non-psychiatrists) to authorize an abortion has been a blatant, premeditated, open-door vehicle by which abortion-on-demand has come to be a reality in several states. Any physician can find three other physicans who will sign a document testifying to the need for an abortion for mental health. Any physician can also find three other physicians who would never sign such a document. This requirement has proved to be totally meaningless.

Medical opinion is deeply divided as to whether psychiatric reasons can ever justify an abortion.

What if a woman has a psychosis, is pregnant, and needs shock treatment. Shouldn't she be aborted?

Pregnancy does not rule out the use of almost any known psychiatric therapy, including electric shock.

But don't some women have psychotic breakdowns after delivering a baby?

Yes. Postpartum psychosis is relatively common following childbirth. It, however, is almost entirely unpredictable. It does not bear any particular relationship to whether or not a woman had mental trouble during her pregnancy. It frequently occurs in a woman who was entirely mentally stable during her pregnancy.

Are there any bad mental after-effects from abortion?

There certainly are. In Chapter Ten we quoted a recent British study reporting on eight maternal abortion deaths, noting that two of them were suicide deaths after the abortion had been performed.

Is this common?

In your authors' experience, we have seen no cases of suicide from refused abortion, but do know of one suicide produced by guilt feelings after an abortion.

Do these guilt feelings come from religious beliefs?

Certainly there are guilt feelings relating to religious beliefs, but most guilt feelings subsequent to abortion have little to do with sectarian religious belief. Abortion violates something very basic in a

41

woman's nature. She normally is the giver of life. Most women who are pregnant are quite aware of the fact that they have a baby growing within them. Most women who have an abortion feel that they have killed their baby. Sometimes there is an almost irresolvable guilt, continuing self reproach, and depression. A good counselor would be of help to a woman during a trying time like this, but the woman who has had an abortion doesn't always come to a counselor.

A wise psychiatrist has said that it is easier to scrape the baby out of the mother's womb than to scrape the thought of that baby out of her mind.

Most guilt feelings aren't religious then?

No. This was well expressed in a letter to the Editor of the A.M.A. News, Aug. 1970, by Mrs. Brian McGivern:

"If guilt feelings are not always permanent, how often? How often and how long will a woman be thankful for the abortionist's actions: through menopause? if she has no more children? when she sees a child whose age would have been her own? If she had the abortion under emotional stress, will she be grateful to the doctors who refused to refer her to a decent agency which could have helped her rather? I would not.

You might not have to hospitalize me for my severe guilt feelings but I'd never forget, after getting out of the stressful situation, that some abortionists have encouraged me to take the easy way out and let me pay the penalty."

Are there any good studies reporting on mental health damage from abortion?

In 1966, the Council of the Royal College of Obstetrics and Gynecology in England reported on a survey of this problem at that time, and said:

"The incidence of serious permanent psychiatric aftermath (from abortion) is variously reported as being from between 9 and 59%."

How about in the United States?

Dr. Paul Gebhart, who did the pioneering work in human sexuality with Dr. Alfred Kinsey and who is known as one of the foremost authorities in this field in the United States, in testifying before the New Jersey legislature in 1968, said that there was evidence of prolonged psychiatric trauma in 9% of a sample of American women who had abortion induced therapeutically or criminally.

I'm not sure that much of this guilt business isn't an unconscious replay of old Christian ethics. How about a non-Christian culture?

Japan has had abortion-on-demand for 22 years and is certainly not a Christian culture. A number of major surveys have been done there in recent years.

In 1963, the Aichi survey reported that 73.1% of women who had been aborted felt "anguish" about what they did.

In 1964, Dr. Tatsuo Kaseki's report stated that 59% felt that abortion was something "very evil" and only 8% thought that it was not "something bad."

In 1969, a major survey by the Prime Minister's Office reported that 88% of women answered that abortion is "bad".

Can you predict who will have psychiatric problems resulting from abortion?

A good evaluation of this comes from Dr. M. Ekblad, whose study in 1955 was reported in Acta Scandinavica, the Swedish medical journal. Sweden, as we know, is a country with very liberal sexual morality standards, and abortion there is not subject to any moral stigma. Dr. Ekblad, however, found that 25% of women having had legal abortions later had "serious regret." In evaluating who might have emotional problems because of abortion, he found a clear relationship. *"The psychiatrically abnormal woman finds it more difficult than the psychologically normal woman to stand the stress of abortion."*

Then the woman in poor mental health is more likely to suffer further psychological harm than the woman who is not upset?

That is exactly what Dr. Ekblad found.

This truism has been a rather well-kept secret from most of our state legislators. While purporting to do abortions for reasons of preserving mental health, in fact, if done on women who are actually psychologically ill, they are being done on the very people to whom they probably will do the most damage psychologically.

Emotional upset, anxiety, fear, strain, and mixed feelings about pregnancy are common, even under the best of circumstances. Pregnancy is not a minor event. Feelings of depression in the early stages of pregnancy are very common. Judgments that the pregnancy and child are unwanted are very common. What is absolutely crucial to understand, however, is that how a woman feels in the first three months of her pregnancy and how she will feel in the last three months of her pregnancy, are commonly totally different. If all upset women with unwanted pregnancies had been aborted in years past, at least one-third of our readers would not be living today. (p 38)

Competent medical opinion is deeply divided as to whether psychiatric reasons ever justify an abortion. The phrase "mental health," written into some of our state laws, has opened a Pandora's box of abortion-on-demand. It bears serious reconsideration by those states that have incorporated this phrase into their laws, and almost certainly it should be stricken from them.

Give more details on Minnesota?

In a detailed report of the Minnesota experience from 1950 - 65 (Minnesota Maternal Mortality Committee, Dept. of OB & Gyn, University of Minnesota,) entitled *"Criminal Abortion Deaths, Illegitimate Pregnancy Deaths, and Suicides in Pregnancy* (American Journal of OB & Gyn, 6/1/67) the following facts are reported:

--- There were only 14 suicides of pregnant women in the state of Minnesota in 15 years, or one for every 93,000 live births. Four were first pregnancies. None were illegitimately pregnant.

--- Ten of these women committed suicide after delivery, only four while pregnant, leading to the author's comment, *"The fetus in utero must be a protective mechanism. Perhaps women are reluctant to take another life with them when they do this."*

--- Twelve of the 14 were p s y c h o t i c depressions. Two were schitzophrenics. Only four had seen a psychiatrist.

--- Male suicides during these years averaged 16 per 100,000 population. Non-pregnant female suicides averaged 3.5 per 100,000 and pregnant female suicides 0.6 per 100,000.

--- The authors conclude that therapeutic abortion for psychiatric reasons *"seems a most nebulous, non-objective, non-scientific approach to medicine. It would seem that psychiatrists would accomplish more by using the available modalities of their speciality in the treatment or rehabilitation of the patient instead of recommending the destruction of another one."*

45

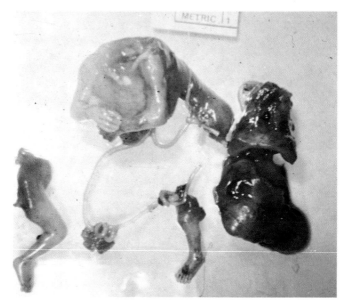

Fig. III by Scraping (with permission, Wm. Hogan, M.D., Rockville, Md.

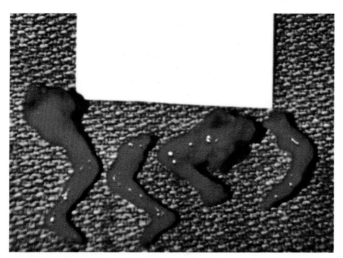

Fig. IV by Suction (with permission, Right to Life League of Southern California)

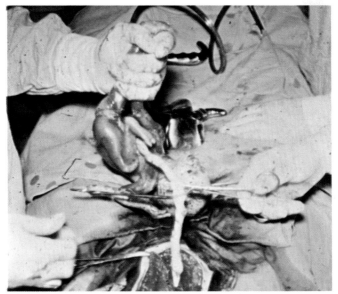

Fig. V Hysterotomy at 24 weeks (with permission, Wm. Hogan, M.D., Rockville, Md.)

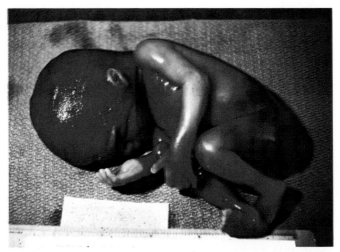

Fig. VI Salt Poisoning at 20 weeks (with permission, Right to Life League of Southern California)

8

UNWANTED CHILD --

RIGHT TO HER OWN BODY

"Editor:

> *I would like to write to you to let you know
> that I am in full accord with the abortions
> that are being performed in New York City.
> For every early physiologic process inter-
> rupted, we are preventing a candidate for our
> relief rolls, our prison population, and our
> growing list of unwanted and frequently bat-
> tered children."*

The above, taken from a letter to the editor
of the A.M.A. News, reflects the thinking of some
people today. If the above were true, the proponents
of abortion at the mother's request would certainly
have added weight to their side of the balance arm of
the scale weighing the value of the life of the unborn
child. If the above is not true, then pro-abortionists
have deluded themselves with more wishful thinking.

I believe every child should be a wanted child, don't you?

We agree that every child should be wanted.
A world without unwanted children would be an
idyllic place in which to live. No one could quarrel
with that as an idealistic goal. Wouldn't it also be a

wonderful world if there were no unwanted wives by husbands, no unwanted aging parents by their children, no unwanted Jews, Black People, Catholics, Chicanos, or ever again a person who at one time or place finds himself unwanted or persecuted. Let's all try to achieve this, but also remember that people have clay feet and, sadly, the unwanted will always be with us.

The measure of our humanity is not that there aren't unwanted ones, but what we do with them. Shall we care for them or kill them?

But why should a mother carry to term an unwanted pregnancy?

Physicians who deliver babies will all agree that a significant percentage of all pregnancies are not planned, and, at the time these women are first seen in the doctor's office, they definitely have "unwanted pregnancies." Overwhelmingly, however, a mother adjusts to the initial surprise and shock, accepts the baby growing within her, and comes to anticipate the birth of her child. After more than twenty years of medical practice, your author personally can say without hesitancy that he has seen many unwanted pregnancies, but has yet to see the first unwanted newborn child. If we permit abortion for an unwanted pregnancy, we will be destroying vast numbers of children, who, by the time of their birth and through their childhood would have been very dearly wanted and deeply loved children indeed. If the judgment of being wanted at an early stage of pregnancy were a final judgment, and abortions were permitted freely, a high percentage of everyone reading this book would never have been born.

But what if a mother delivered a baby that she really didn't want?

The federal judges who, in January, 1971, ruled the Ohio abortion law to be constitutional spoke very eloquently to this. They said:

> *"Equating the necessity of giving birth to a child with the necessity of rearing the child has no foundation in law or fact. The law may take permanently from its natural parents a child who is neglected by them, and the frequent hesitancy of courts and social agencies in this regard does not change the legal situation. Statutes of practically all states provide for the voluntary surrender of children. When the statutes are complied with, the child is legally and practically as dead to its natural parents as if it had been aborted, stillborn, or had died in infancy. The validity and effectiveness of surrender statutes has been upheld in every case in which they have been questioned. There is no need for parents to terminate an undesired pregnancy by killing the unborn child physically when with less risk to themselves, its legal death can so easily be procured."*

The opening letter assumes that all unwanted pregnancies will be neglected children. Is that a valid assumption?

That assumption is almost too naive and simplistic to be given any serious consideration. The fact that it has been mentioned again and again is almost beyond comprehension. Most unwanted pregnancies become wanted babies. Some wanted children become unwanted ones. Unloved babies sometimes become dearly loved and vice versa. To make the assumption that because a woman is unwillingly pregnant, the child in every case, in most cases, or even in many cases will be unwanted and therefore neglected and abused, is totally inaccurate and wildly unrealistic. Some will, of course, but many will not. Why kill them all before birth? Why not sort them out after birth, strengthen our laws that the court mentions above, and take unwanted children from parents who are unworthy to raise them?

48

The woman in the Ohio court case said that if her baby was delivered that she would batter it. What about that?

The logical answer, of course, is to take the child from her at birth and to give the baby to adoptive parents who would love and care for him.

But don't many unwanted pregnancies become battered children?

Many would think so. In fact, this is not true. Dr. Edward Lenoski, Professor of Pediatrics at the University of Southern California, did a four-and-a-half year study of 400 battered children. He determined that 90% of the battered children in his study were planned pregnancies. Ninety percent is far above average for planned pregnancies. Most of our readers undoubtably deeply cherish and love the children that they have been given. How many of you, however, actually planned the conception of 90% of them? We could apparently kill all "unwanted" babies in the early stages of pregnancy, but still not significantly reduce the numbers of battered children.

Dr. Lenoski has also determined that since the advent of the contraceptive pill (which has certainly reduced unwanted pregnancies), child beating is up threefold.

What of the right of a woman to the privacy of her own body?

At least one pro-abortion court decision has referred to this. We think it is an entirely fallacious bit of reasoning. If you, as a citizen, stand outside of a door and listen to a mother battering her child, even to the point of killing it, what would you do? Would you respect the privacy of her home? You would not! You would open or break down the door and rescue the child. By virtue of her assault upon and abuse of another human person, she has surrendered her constitutional right to privacy in this case. The same analogy applies to abortion. The right of the child to live is greater than and supersedes any right that a woman may have to the privacy of her own body.

But a woman does have a right to her own body. Isn't the child, at least in the early stages of pregnancy, part of her body?

A woman's appendix, obviously a part of her body, can be removed for sufficient reason. The cells of the appendix, however, carry the identical genetic code that is present in every other cell in the mother's body. They are, for this reason, undeniably part of her body. The single-celled fertilized ovum or the multi-celled zygote or later developing embryonic human being within her uterus cannot, by any stretch of the imagination, be considered part of her body. This new living being has a genetic code that is totally different from the cells of the mother's body. It is, in truth, a completely separate growing organism and can never be considered part of the mother's body. Does she have a right to her own body? Yes. But this is not part of her own body. It is another person's body.

No right at all?

The Rev. Charles Carroll, Protestant chaplain of the University of California at Berkeley, student of International Law at Yale, Harvard, and the University of Berlin during the Hitler period, and officer of the United States military government in Germany at the trial of the Nazi doctors at Nuremberg, has stated:

> *"As I would reject the law of paterfamilias of ancient Rome, so I would also reject the proposed law of materfamilias in present day America. As I would not sympathize with the grant by the state*

of the power of life and death of his offspring to the Roman father, so I cannot sympathize with the grant by any state of the power of life and death over her offspring to the American mother. Surely I would hope our legislators would be as humane as the Emperor Hadrian, who abolished that article of the Roman Law."

9

POPULATION EXPLOSION?

"The Census Bureau announced yesterday a major downward revision of its population projections for the next thirty years.

It is possible, the Bureau said, that there will be nearly 100,000,000 fewer Americans in the year 2000 than had been forecast in one maximum projection made just three years ago.

The revised projections are based on the dramatic decline in U.S. birth rates experienced in the United States in the Sixties. The birth rate in 1968, for example, was the lowest in American history."

— Washington Post, August 13, 1970

Most peoples' reaction to the above was, "What's going on here?" For years we've been told that it won't be long until there's standing room only on the earth."

Population explosion very definitely has a place in our discussion about abortion. One of the major reasons given to justify new and liberalized abortion laws is the pressure of unwanted population. Let's look at some of these facts.

What is the population of the United States?

The 1970 U.S. Census count placed the U.S. population at 204.7 million.

Isn't this a substantial increase in the last decade?

In total numbers of people, it was the second largest in U.S. history, having declined from the total number added between 1950 and 1960. In the percentage of gain, however, it was the second lowest rate of increase of any decade in the history of the United States. Only the depression years of the 1930's were lower.

How many children should the average family have in order to stabilize population growth?

In 1850, the average number of children per family in the United States was 6.0. In 1970, the average number of children per family was 2.45, and dropping. Taking into account a slowly increasing death rate in this country, as our population bulge approaches old age, population growth will stop altogether between 2.1 and 2.2 children per family. This would be zero growth rate.

What about population trends? Can't they tell us accurately what will happen?

Population trends are notoriously subject to both mistakes and abuse in predicting any distance in the future. See Fig. VII, p. 54.)

--- In 1910, there were 30.1 children born in the United States for every 1000 people. In 1936, this had dropped to 18.4. If this trend had continued, births in the United States would have ceased altogether by 1975.

--- In 1936, the birth rate was 18.4 per 1000. In 1957, the birth rate had risen to 25.3 per 1000. If this trend had continued, we would have had over 400 million people by the year 2000, almost a billion by 2050, and two-and-a-half billion by 2100.

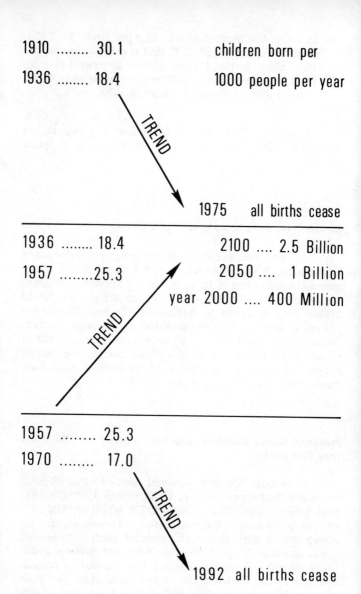

| 1910 .... 30.1 | children born per |
| 1936 .... 18.4 | 1000 people per year |

TREND

1975   all births cease

1936 .... 18.4	2100 .... 2.5 Billion
1957 ....25.3	2050 .... 1 Billion
	year 2000 .... 400 Million

TREND

| 1957 .... 25.3 |
| 1970 .... 17.0 |

TREND

1992   all births cease

Fig. VII   Population Trends

54

--- In 1957, the birth rate was 25.3 per 1000. By 1970, it had dropped to 17.0. If this trend continues, the last baby in the United States to ever utter its first cry after birth, will be born in the year 1992, and further births will cease totally.

It seems obvious that extending any population trend very far into the future can prove to be quite inaccurate.

But can't we make some kind of prediction?

As you can see from the above, predictions are hazardous. It would seem safe, however, and it is the general concensus of opinion among almost everyone, that births per family and per woman in the United States will continue to decline in the next five to ten years. It is on the basis of this that Mr. George Brown, Director of the United States Census Bureau, said in October of 1970: *"Instead of the loudly proclaimed people explosion in the United States, current population trends could result in a zero growth rate."*

President Nixon appointed a group to study this. What did they find out?

President Nixon's National Goals Research Staff released its report in July, 1970, entitled, "TOWARD BALANCED GROWTH: QUANTITY WITH QUALITY" (U. S. Government Printing Office, Washington, D. C., 20042, $1.50 per copy). It reported that, *"If present trends continue for just ten more years, our national population growth will stop altogether. The question of population size in the United States is not Malthusian. The issue is not whether we can feed and clothe a population of any size we can realistically envisage, or even supply it with the expanding amount of energy it may demand."*

What of the death rate? Does this influence population size?

The U.S. death rate is now 9.6 per 1,000 people per year. As our population grows older and more people reach old age, the death rate will eventually rise to about fifteen per 1,000 per year, assuming our life expectancy holds at 70 years.

How many people will we have in the United States in the year 2000?

If our current birth rate stabilizes at its present level, we will have a population of 281 million in the year 2000. If it continues to decline, it could be much less.

Since the rate is dropping, then why this rather substantial increase from our present 204 million?

This is because the babies born during the post-war baby boom of the early Fifties constitute a population "bulge" as they now come of marriageable age. This excess in numbers of people of this one age group will be forming their families and having children, thus producing an overall jump in total number of people, even though the percentage per family continues to drop. When this bulge, however, is past, if current trends continue, the population growth will flatten and probably reach zero growth rate.

How many babies are actually born in the United States in a year?

In 1957, there were 4,308,000 babies born. In 1968, there were 3,470,000 babies born. We are already educating that excess of births from the late Fifties. Our schools are crowded with them. This bulge is passing, however. In 1976, for instance, there will be 800,000 fewer third graders in the nation's classrooms than there are today. This, at least, is not guesswork. These babies have already been born. We can look forward to an overabundance of teachers, schools, and educational facilities in the decade of the Seventies.

You believe that families will be smaller in the future?

In a Gallup Poll (Feb., 1971) the question was asked: *"Would you like four or more children in your family?"*

in 1967 -- 40% answered "Yes"

in 1971 -- 23% answered "Yes"

Of great importance was that, of all the college-educated, only 14% wanted four or more. Of those with only a grade school education, 33% wanted four or more.

This is further confirmation, if any is needed, that the only way to effectively limit population growth is to raise a group's standard of living and education.

Abortion is being spoken of as a means of population control. What does the medical profession think of this?

The official statement of the American College of Obstetrics and Gynecology in 1968 said: *"It is firmly stated that the College will not condone nor support the concept that abortion be considered or performed as a means of population control."*

Isn't the increase of population in our cities the cause for the rise in violent crime, illegitimacy, etc.?

Our cities have a population implosion. This is due to a poor distribution of people, not the simple fact of national over-population itself.

In Holland, the population density is 1,000 people per square mile. In the United States it is 57 people per square mile. Even taking into account the vast waste areas of mountains, etc., in the United States, the only areas that approach Holland in population density are those of our crowded cities. Yet it is well known that Holland has only a fraction of the crime rate and social upset of our major cities.

As another example, Great Britain has 50 million people living in an area smaller than California. Why is it then, that there are fewer murders on the entire British Isles annually than there are in the city of Chicago, or Cleveland, or even of Greater Kansas City? Obviously, population density in itself does not produce high crime rates and social upset.

Won't too many people increase the problem of pollution?

Certainly, more people produce more pollution. Certainly, more affluent people produce more pollution per person than poor people. However, more wealthy and more educated people also produce the wealth and technology to combat pollution. The basic problem is not the simple fact of people existing, but of education, of methods of industrial production, of self-discipline, etc.

What will remedy our pollution problems?

Not merely the simplistic answer of reducing the number of children per family. We could stop population growth, and our rivers would still be ecological slums, the air over our cities would still remain unbreathable, and our environment would continue to deteriorate. What is needed is massive efforts, great sums of money, educational campaigns, and in many ways, a substantial change in the way we live, not in how many of us are alive.

What will the effects of population growth in our country do to the economics of this country?

The Wall Street Journal (Dec., 1970) said: *"Population projections for the 1970's indicate a further decline in the growth rate. Our big population explosion is in the past, but the echo effects will reverberate strongly throughout the economy for many years to come. Census experts believe American families in general will enjoy rapidly rising incomes in the years ahead. Median family income is expected to rise from around $9,900 today to $15,000 in 1985, measured in dollars of constant purchasing power."*

The other thing the Journal pointed out was that the labor force in the United States will be increasing much faster than the population, as the bulge of young people moves into their working, productive adult years. A labor Department report says of this: *"The large numbers of young workers may provide an abundance of new ideas. The eagerness, imagination, and flexibility of the young will contribute to developing new ways of business organization, production, and marketing."* Needless to say, they will also find new ways of attacking and solving our pollution problems.

How much space is there actually existing at this time for every person who lives in the United States?

If we divide the number of people presently living in the United States by its total acreage, each individual has ten acres.

What percentage of the population of the U.S. is needed to produce the food we eat?

Less than 5%.

What of the world population? Will it follow the same trends as the United States?

One thing is certain. Neither voluntary birth control nor abortion has ever stopped the population growth of an economically underdeveloped and underprivileged country. One sure way to slow down population growth of underdeveloped countries is to bring them up to an increased standard of living. As we increase the standard of living of a nation, its people will voluntarily limit their family size. This is the major problem for the rest of the world in the decades ahead.

Won't the rest of the world outgrow its food supply?

A few years ago, dire predictions of this were being made. Within the last several years, however, a "green revolution" has occurred. Hybrid wheat, corn, and rice have been developed that have radically changed the outlook in these hungry lands. In Pakistan, wheat output has soared from four-and-a-half to twelve-and-a-half million tons in just five years. In India, wheat production has gone from twelve-and-a-half to nineteen-and-a-half million tons in five years. The same has happened to rice within several years. At present rates, most of the teeming sub-continent of Asia will be exporting grain rather than needing our help to stave off starvation. Their remaining problem is distribution of food, not production of it.

What is the opinion of major candidates for the 1972 Presidential election?

President Richard Nixon on April 3, 1971, said:

"I consider abortion an unacceptable form of population control. Further, unrestricted abortion policies, or abortion on demand, I cannot square with my personal belief in the sanctity of human life — including the life of the yet unborn. For, surely, the unborn have rights also, recognized in

law, recognized even in principles expounded by the United Nations.

"Ours is a nation with a Judeo-Christian heritage. It is also a nation with serious social problems — problems of malnutrition, of broken homes, of poverty and of delinquency. But none of these problems justifies such a solution.

"A good and generous people will not opt, in my view, for this kind of alternative to its social dilemmas. Rather, it will open its hearts and homes to the unwanted children of its own, as it has done for the unwanted millions of other lands."

Senator Edmund Muskie, the same week said on a T.V. show:

"I'm concerned about diluting in any way the concept of the sanctity of life.

"First of all, we're not entirely sure of the psychological impact upon mothers themselves who become free or indiscriminate in the use of this way of avoiding the consequences of sexual relations.

"A life has been taken away from them, and it's the very nature of motherhood, you know, to shield and protect life, not to destroy it . . . If it becomes all right to take a life in that stage, then how easy will it be to slip into the next step. Should people in old age who are senile — does it then become legitimate to take their lives? And there is the medical question of when does life begin to quicken. That, I guess is about six weeks . . . it's when you get beyond that point that I begin to have trouble."

10

HOW MANY MOTHERS DIE FROM LEGAL ABORTIONS?

"We can look forward to this (legal abortion) being the dominant cause of death to young women."

- The Scotsman, March 9, 1970

The above statement by Professor Ian Donald, Professor of Midwifery, Glasgow University, is the sort of news that has simply not been printed by our country's newspapers, popular magazines, etc., intent as they seem to be on the headlong rush toward legalization of abortion in this country. Professor Donald made the above statement when he reported on 20,000 legal abortions in England in 1969, which had resulted in the deaths of fifteen mothers. More simply stated, this means that there was almost one death for every 1,000 legal abortions. To say the least, this is an extremely sobering fact, and demonstrates the fallacy of the oft-repeated statement of Dr. Alan Gutenmacher, President of Planned Parenthood, that legal abortions are "magnificently safe." It is common today to read the statements of all sorts of uninformed people who say that delivery of a child is more dangerous to the mother than a legal abortion. This is simply not true. Abortion of any type, at any stage of pregnancy, is a serious operation, serious for the health and life of the mother, and serious in its future implications to her as a woman and potential mother in years ahead.

What has been Sweden's experience regarding maternal deaths?

Sweden does not have a complete abortion-on-demand law, but is relatively selective of its abortions. Under these circumstances, in a country where medical care is as excellent as anywhere in the world, the maternal death rate is forty per 100,000 abortions, or four deaths per 10,000 abortions.

What about closer to home?

Magee Hospital for Women in Pittsburgh in 1970 had three mothers become desperately ill after legal abortions with one dying in spite of 30 units of blood, and hemodialysis, out of almost 900 abortions. (Personal Communication)

In Maryland, from June 1969 to June 1970, the official figures show three mothers dying from 3867 abortions. (ABORTION SURVEILLANCE REPORT, Maryland Department of Health.)

New York's 1970 figures are very confusing at this point. Different agencies are reporting very contradictory statistics and it is well known that a large percentage of the abortions done outside of accredited hospitals and their maternal toll have not been reported at all. It would be impossible to draw any conclusions yet from the New York experience except to point out that, since many women come from out of state with no possibility of follow-up, accurate statistics may never be available.

How many mothers die in childbirth today?

Simply reading or quoting officially published "maternal mortality" figures is misleading. Why? Because all abortion deaths are *included* in maternal mortality figures, as well as a number of women who die during or after pregnancy of kidney disease, accidents, high blood pressure, and stroke conditions that might have claimed them whether they were pregnant or not. When we speak of the actual number of mothers who have died directly because of the process of childbirth (as abortion deaths are figured), we frequently see series of 10,000 or more consecutive deliveries before finding a mother who dies in childbirth. Average actual childbirth deaths in our country are about two mothers for every 10,000 births. For example, in a series of almost 60,000 deliveries at the Good Samaritan Hospital in Cincinnati between 1955-56, the maternal death rate was 1.84 per 10,000 deliveries (compared with Sweden's 4.0, England's 7.5, and Maryland's 7.7 per 10,000 abortions).

Is delivering a baby safer than having an abortion if both are done under the best of circumstances?

Yes. Delivering a baby is at least twice as safe in terms of the mother's life as having an abortion under the best of circumstances. Another example would be to compare Minnesota, with 1.4 mothers dying per 10,000 deliveries, to Sweden, with 4.0 dying per 10,000 abortions.

But I have heard a figure from Hungary of only two deaths in over 300,000 abortions.

This was an "official" figure released through the Communist government of Hungary. It would claim that the medical care in that unfortunate country, crushed under an exploiting and dictatorial Communist regime, is sixty times better than that in Sweden, Britain, or the United States. This is too absurd to even consider, and is propaganda at its most blatant. Unless statistics are thoroughly and impartially documented and reported without "clearance" through such a government, they are worse than useless.

What is the cause of death in mothers who have legal abortions?

A report in the British Medical Journal, May 1970, reported a series of eight maternal abortion deaths. The causes were as follows:

Blood clot in lung	– two cases
Anesthetic death	– one case
Heart	– one case
Cause unknown	– one case
Complication, illegal abortion	– one case
Suicide following legal abortion	– two cases

What does the American College of Obstetrics and Gynecology say about the safety of abortions?

Their official statement in May of 1968 said: *"It is emphasized that the inherent risk of an abortion is not fully appreciated, both by many in the profession, and certainly not by the public."*

What does the New York State Medical Society say?

New York State Medical Society Guidelines of July 1, 1970, include the statement: *"Abortion performed after the twelfth week is fraught with tremendous danger."*

Most New York abortions have been performed in Greater New York City. What do the physicians of the area think of this in terms of danger to the mother?

After four months experience with the New York law, the five county medical societies of Greater New York City unanimously recommended that abortions not be performed after the twelfth week; that they not be done on an out-patient basis; and that they be limited only to hospitals or clinics which would be required to have special equipment, such as blood transfusion services, etc., available.

Are all legal abortion deaths of mothers reported in the city where they were aborted?

Definitely not. Some mothers who have been aborted in New York City have gone home to die. In the case of such a mother who became ill and died after returning to her home state, as a direct result of the abortion which she had had, her death would not be included among the statistics of New York state, but rather in her own state. A major cause of these deaths is blood transfusions.

Blood transfusions are a cause of death in abortions?

Yes, very much so, and these deaths never are associated directly, nor reported as statistics related to abortions. Here's how this works:

For every 1,000 units (pints) of blood transfused, one pint will carry a virus that is serious enough to ultimately cause a fatal hepatitis in the person who receives it. Receiving one unit of blood has the same mortality as having your appendix removed. If a woman hemorrhages during an abortion procedure, and many do, she will seldom need only one unit of blood; she will usually need three or four, or even more pints of blood. If we would take four pints as the average number needed for the woman who hemorrhages, then it is evident that of every 250 women transfused, one will die within the next several months of infectious hepatitis. Her death will be listed as being from hepatitis, not abortion.

How many women who have had abortions die as a result of the transfusions needed?

Dr. W. Droegemuller, reporting in the American Journal of Obstetrics and Gynecology, Mar. 1969, on the first year experience of Colorado, reported that eight out of every 100 women who were aborted needed blood transfusions. Others report less than this, some as little as one woman transfused out of every 100 or more abortions performed. Probably, a conservative average is about one or two per 100 abortions done. If one woman (see above) in every 250 who are transfused ultimately dies of hepatitis, and one woman in every fifty or 100 who is aborted needs blood transfusions, then there are an additional four to eight maternal deaths per 100,000 abortions, in addition to those reported in official vital statistics as abortion deaths.

You're talking about the maternal deaths caused by abortion. What about all the women who would die by suicide if abortion were refused them?

The suicide rate for pregnant women is less than one-fourth that among the general female population of similar age group.

As Dr. B. Sloan of Temple University has said, *"Suicide is rare"* among pregnant women.

There aren't many suicides then?

Many well-informed counselors in the profession are of the opinion that there are probably at least as many and possibly more suicides resulting from guilt and emotional upset because of an abortion as there are among those women who cannot obtain an abortion. (See pp. 40, 65)

What is the fetal mortality rate in abortions? (How many unborn babies die?)

Almost one hundred percent. One tiny girl aborted in New York did not die as planned and has been adopted. Within the medical profession, cases of live babies being born from abortion are becoming common. (See pp. 4, 28 and 110)

11

PHYSICAL HARM
FROM ABORTION?

It was estimated that hepatitis kills four to eight out of every 100,000 mothers who have an abortion. Does hepatitis have harmful effects in others who get the disease but recover?

For every one woman who has hepatitis severe enough to be fatal, there are dozens of women who have milder cases of hepatitis, with resulting lengthy illnesses and often some degree of permanent loss of physical health and stamina.

What other bad effects come to the mother from abortion?

There are only a few lengthy, rigidly controlled scientific studies in large groups of women. The largest of these come from Japan, where abortion has been legal for 22 years. These are not the highly sophisticated, control group, double blind, etc., studies we are familiar with in our country, but they do reflect the opinion of literally millions of women who were asked questions as to how they felt after having had abortions. In the 1959 Mainichi Survey, 28% of those who had had abortions reported "some kind of bad effect." In the 1963 Aichi Survey, 13% indicated damage from the operation. In the 1964 Welfare Ministry Survey, 24% indicated they were physically unwell since the operation. In the 1968 Nagoia Survey by the Women's Association, 59% indicated that they were severly troubled with adverse after-effects, or in less than good health. In the

1969 Survey by the Office of the Prime Minister, 31% indicated that some kind of physical abnormality came about as the result of an abortion. This averages 29% in six major surveys. In the Mainichi Survey, the percentage of complaints rose with the number of abortions per woman. 18% said they were physically unwell after one operation, 22% after two, 40% after three, and 51% after four.

Those are impressive percentages. But what kind of damage are they talking about?

The 1969 Survey of the Office of the Prime Minister of Japan listed the following complaints after abortion:

1) 9% sterility

2) 14% subsequent habitual spontaneous miscarriage

3) 400% increase in tubal pregnancies

4) 17% menstrual irregularities

5) 20-30% abdominal pain, dizziness, headaches, etc.

How much of the headache, etc., type complaints were specifically caused by abortion would be difficult to say. The sterility, tubal pregnancy, and subsequent miscarriage figures are essentially what have been reported in surveys in other countries.

An increase in tubal pregnancies after a legal abortion?

Yes. The suction and scraping of the inside of the womb, while cutting up and removing the unborn baby, must cause some scarring so that later the fertilized egg cannot move normally down and out of the tube to nest in the wall of the womb. The growing new human baby (zygote) then nests and starts to grow in the mother's tube. Within a few weeks, this causes an acute abdominal condition in the mother, with internal hemorrhage necessitating an emergency operation and removal of the tube.

Tubal pregnancies are four times more common among those who have had abortions, as compared to those who have not.

What about miscarriages later?

The Japanese report states that after having had an abortion, about one out of every seven women who subsequently became pregnant, who would not have normally miscarried, did have a spontaneous miscarriage, and continued to have habitual miscarriages in later pregnancies. This is a higher percentage than some studies, but lower than some others. It can certainly be said that there is a substantial increase in spontaneous miscarriages in women who have had induced abortions.

The report mentioned sterility. Do you mean that once you've had an abortion, it's harder to get pregnant in the future even if you want to?

That is exactly what the report says. Some older women would not mind if they become sterile, but most abortions are done in young ladies who do want to have children in the future. In a cross-section of the general population, about 10-15% of all marriages will be childless for a wide variety of reasons. For couples who marry, where the woman has had one abortion, there will be probably an additional 5% sterility in these couples and with each additional abortion, the figure rises higher yet.

What are some of the other physical problems encountered from abortion?

Other damage to the mother includes perforation of the uterus with the curette, resulting in peritonitis and occasional death, but more frequently, emergency removal of the uterus, and often development of adhesions that may give problems in later life.

Adherent placenta (afterbirth) is another problem. Normally at delivery, the placenta separates easily from the inside of the womb, and is delivered very soon after the baby. In some women who have had induced abortions, the placenta becomes adherent to the inside wall of the uterus, does not separate normally, produces hemmorhage, and sometimes necessitates its surgical removal.

Are blood clots ever a problem?

Blood clots are one of the causes of death to mothers who deliver babies normally. They are also a cause of death in healthy young women who have abortions performed. In the English study reported in the previous chapter, one out of four mothers who died from abortions did so from blood clots.

Embolism (floating objects in the blood that go to the lungs) is another problem. Childbirth is a normal process, and the body is well prepared for the birth of the child and the separation and expulsion of the placenta. Surgical abortion is an abnormal process, and scrapes the unripe placenta from the wall of the uterus where its roots have grown. This sometimes causes the fluid around the baby, or other pieces of tissue, or blood clots, to be forced into the mother's circulation. These then travel to her lungs, causing damage and occasional death. This is also the chief cause of maternal death from the saline method of abortion.

These complications make it sound like abortion is more dangerous than delivering a baby. That's not what I've been reading.

The above figures speak for themselves. Many people who are in favor of abortion are honest and well-intentioned. Unfortunately, a great many of those favoring abortion simply do not know the facts, choose to ignore them, or brush over them in their eagerness to convince our society that destroying unborn human lives would solve many of our problems. If we actually compare similar age groups of women who have had induced abortions and women who have delivered babies, we find that it is much more damaging to their physical health to have an abortion.

Is there any risk to the baby if, after having an abortion, a woman wants to have a child?

Aside from the problems mentioned above, of increased miscarriage, etc., the major problem is increased number of premature babies born. The average number of babies that are born "premie" is five out of each 100 babies.

Dr. Ian Donald of Glasgow University reports that the prematurity rate among women who have had previous abortions has risen to an "alarming" rate of 15% of all deliveries. There is no reason to assume that our experience in the United States will be any different than that in other countries.

> *"Prematurity was a direct or contributory cause in over 50% of deaths during the first month of life. The death rate of the premature baby ran about thirty times higher than among full-term infants. If premature infants survive, they face a higher frequency of the tragic aftermath of mental retardation, neurologic diseases and blindness."*
>
> The Challenge of Prematurity
> Dennis Cavanaugh, M.D.
> Medical World News, Feb. 1971

It is entirely possible, in states that have abortion on demand, that the number of defective babies killed by abortion will be more than supplanted by a greater number of defective babies, caused by prematurity, which is a direct result of the previous legal abortions of their mothers.

Why this increase in prematurity?

When an abortion is done, the cervical muscle must be stretched open to allow the surgeon to enter the uterus. In a D & C for a spontaneous miscarriage, no harm is done as the cervix is usually soft and even open. The same is usually true for the D & C done on a women for excessive menstruation, etc. When however, a normal, well rooted placenta and growing baby are scraped out of a firmly closed uterus, protected by a long, "green" cervical muscle, the task of dilating this muscle is more difficult. Undoubtedly some muscle fibers are torn, permanently weakening it. Stanford University Hospital, for example, reported:

> *"In our hospital amongst nulliparous (first pregnancy) patients undergoing suction curetage for therapeutic abortion, about one in eight required suture (stitches) of the cervix because of laceration occurring during the process of dilitation."* (R.C. Goodlin, M.D., OB-Gyn Collected Letters of the International Correspondence Society of Obstetricians and Gynecologists, p. 97, June 15, 1971.)

Probably this weakening at times results in an "incompetent cervix" which will open prematurely, causing premature birth, as it is not strong enough to hold the heavier weight of a full term child. It may also be partly responsible for the increase of later spontaneous miscarriage seen after legal abortions.

What of Rh problems?

Legal abortion can sensitize a mother so that in later pregnancies her babies will have Rh problems, need transfusions, and occasionally be born dead or die after birth. This can be tested for and largely prevented by giving a very expensive medication called Rhogam. Unfortunately, many of the abortion mills now operating "legally" in New York and other states do not take this expensive precaution.

12

REDUCE ILLEGAL

ABORTION?

"Women should not be subjected to back room kitchen-table butchery. Thousands of married women as well as single girls die every year because the law has driven them to attic hideouts and motel room surgery."

Ann Landers
The Cincinnati Post & Times-Star
December 23, 1969

Who would argue?

No one would defend the crude abortion done by an unqualified person in unsterile surroundings. The above argument is a very powerful one, and has been used with telling effect on legislators throughout the United States. If it were true, it would be a very strong argument indeed in favor of at least some legalization of abortion. The problem is that our esteemed columnist has been misinformed, and so has most of America. Her concern is shared by us all but, legalizing abortion does not, has not, and apparently will not reduce the number of illegal abortions.

How about Sweden? Hasn't it reduced illegal abortions there?

No, it hasn't. Sweden is generally considered to have one of the more "enlightened and progressive laws." The prestigious British Medical Journal

Lancet, in 1968 in a report entitled "On the Outcome of Pregnancy When Legal Abortion Is Readily Available" stated: *"Sweden's law, in its present form, has not sufficed to subdue criminal abortion."*

Dr. Christopher Tietze, certainly one of the world's outstanding biostaticians, and a man who incidentally favors legalization of abortion, has written in his report, "Abortion In Europe:" *"One of the major goals of the liberalization laws in Scandinavia was to reduce illegal abortion. This was not realized. Rather, as we know from a variety of sources, both criminal and total abortions increased. It survives because of the relative lack of privacy of the official procedures."*

(U.S. JOURNAL OF PUBLIC HEALTH, Nov. 1967.)

Was this also true of Japan?

Even more so in Japan. Of the 50,000,000 unborn children that have been killed by abortions in the last 22 years in Japan, and where abortions are very inexpensive, a full one-third of the procedures continue to be done illegally.

What of the United States? What has been our experience to date?

There hasn't been too much published because legalized abortion laws are new in our country. Dr. W. Droegemuller in the American Journal of Obstetrics and Gynecology, March 1969, reporting on "One Year Experience With a Liberalized Abortion Law," says that, *"This has not reduced the admissions for septic abortions."* Sepsis (infection) is one of the most common complications of criminal abortion, and the number of septic cases admitted post-abortive to a hospital is a fairly good indication in a community of the number of criminal abortions being done.

But perhaps their laws are too restrictive. What if abortion is completely available at the request of the mother? Wouldn't that eliminate illegal abortions?

It didn't in Japan. It hasn't in England nor in any other major country to date.

What is the reason why illegal abortions are not reduced?

Here are some examples:

1) Suppose you are the wife of a man who wants another child. You do not. You become pregnant. If you go through official procedures in a hospital, your husband may find out. You don't want him to know, but you want to get rid of this baby, so you have an illegal abortion.

2) Suppose you are a married woman, and you become pregnant by another man. Your husband has been away, and he knows this would not be his child. Again, he must never know that you've become pregnant, so you have it done illegally.

3) Suppose you are a prominent citizen, and your teenage daughter becomes pregnant. You wish to avoid scandal. Hospital procedures are available to her. You cannot, however, take the risk of disclosure. You have it done in the privacy of an illegal situation.

4) Suppose you are poor. Perhaps your man has left you. There is a long waiting list at the public hospital, and much red tape you don't understand. You are frantic to "get rid of it." A friend tells you of someone who will. You go there.

All of the above tell the same story: fear of disclosure, of someone finding out, or of ignorance. In order to make abortions as safe as it is possible to make them, there must be official and scientific supervision, rules, and public inspection. Whether privacy would be violated or not is beside the point. People universally in this country and elsewhere, fear that it might, and so, no matter how available legal abortions may be made, people in large numbers will continue to seek illegal ones and suffer the consequences.

I've heard that 8,000 to 20,000 mothers die every year from illegal abortions.

Christopher Tietze, probably the world's most eminent biostatician, has called this figure "unmitigated nonsense."

The Vital Statistics of the U.S. Public Health Department list the following number of deaths from abortion, legal and illegal combined, in the entire United States:

in 1942 there were 1232

in 1947 there were 583

in 1957 there were 260

in 1968 there were 130

Is this accurate?

Perhaps a few can be covered up, but not many. These figures essentially reflect the actual state of affairs. For instance, the Ohio State Medical Association reported that deaths in Ohio from abortions have averaged 6.5 annually over the last decade.

The above figures of "total abortion deaths" will rise sharply as soon as the mothers dying from the rapidly increasing legal abortions since 1968 are added. Because deaths from illegal abortions will not decline, legal abortion deaths will be added to the above numbers, raising them substantially.

What of England? Hasn't the number of illegal abortions dropped there?

The most authoritative report on this was published in the British Medical Journal, May 1970, by the Royal College of Obstetrics and Gynecology, and constituted a summary of the opinions of the consultant obstetricians of England. It said:

> *"The original protagonists for abortion law reform often argued that a large proportion of cases of spontaneous abortions hitherto treated in hospitals and nearly all the associated deaths were the result of criminal interference. Legalization of abortion would, they postulated, eliminate these. They brushed aside contrary arguments and evidence. Our figures show . . . that despite a sharp rise in the number of therapeutic ('legal') abortions from 1968 to 1969, there was not, unfortunately, a significant change in the number of cases of spontaneous abortion requiring admission to hospital.*

> *"The fact that legalization of abortion has not so far materially reduced the numbers of spontaneous abortions or of deaths from abortions of all kinds is not surprising. It confirms the experience of most countries and was forecast by the College's 1966 statement."*

13

DEFORMITY OF THE CHILD (PRE-NATAL EUTHANASIA)

All of the reasons discussed so far, that have been put forward as justification for abortion, have been so-called maternal indications. They have related directly to the mother, her life, her health, her social or economic well-being, her convenience. In all of them, the physical intactness and perfection, or otherwise, of the growing child within her has not been considered. The consideration has been whether she has wanted to bear a child at all. When considering abortion for deformity of the child, we are only peripherally thinking of the mother, who might well sustain certain anguish if she bears such a child. Rather, we are thinking primarily of the child himself, and are asking whether this child has an intact enough mind and body to justify his continued life.

With this thinking we enter an entirely new rationale for justification of the existence of a life. In this case the price tag on the life of this unborn child, the justification for allowing him to live and to be born, is whether or not he will prove independent enough, intelligent enough, and useful enough to society to allow him to live. We cannot emphasize strongly enough that this is an entirely different set of criteria than maternal indications for abortion. It introduces an entirely new set of values into our western civilization's regard for human life.

Why is this such a different value judgment than the previous maternal indications discussed?

Quite simply, this judgment says that a human life should not be permitted to continue to live if that human life does not measure up to a certain degree of physical and mental perfection and/or is not independent and useful to those around him, including the state. This is an absolutely frightening concept. Only three decades ago this value judgment was applied on a large scale by the German state, a story too gruesome to recount.

But Hitler only killed Jews, didn't he?

He ended by trying to eliminate what he called a "defective" race. However, he began some years earlier with abortion, infanticide, and euthanasia to eliminate those whom he termed "useless eaters." He "cleaned out" the asylums for mentally defective children, the psychotically defective adults, and the senile defective old people. All of these were pure blood Aryans, members of his "master race," but not useful to the state, and because of this, they were killed. His next step was to eliminate a "defective" race, the Jews.

Why drag in that Hitler business again? I don't know anybody who agreed with his slaughter of the Jews, but I know plenty of people who would agree with aborting a mentally defective child. How can you associate the two?

When life before birth can be destroyed because it will not be a fruitful and productive life, and that becomes law of the land, there is no logic or rational line to draw between the killing of pre-born children because they're defective, and the killing of a post-born child because it is defective. This is called infanticide or newborn euthanasia, as opposed to the abortion approach which is correctly called prenatal euthanasia.

Once a policy and an acceptance of euthanasia for a defective human life has been established at one stage in human life, then it will be easy to accept euthanasia at other stages of human life as well.

Are there any examples?

Yes. In England, only six months after their permissive abortion law was passed, a law legalizing euthanasia barely missed passage. Other states in the U.S. are considering introducing euthanasia bills, in fact, in Florida, in 1969 and 1970, a bill to legalize euthanasia was defeated in the state legislature. It was reintroduced in 1971 by Representative Sackett.

Who has spoken to this?

New York Assemblyman, Martin Gainsburg, in April of 1969, in pleading that the abortion-on-demand bill in New York not be passed, said the following:

"What this bill says is that those who are malformed or abnormal have no reason to be part of our society. If we are prepared to say that a life should not come into this world malformed or abnormal, then tomorrow we should be prepared to say that a life already in this world which becomes malformed or abnormal should not be permitted to live."

The Rabbinical Council of America recently said:

"Even if the fetus is the product of incest or rape, or an abnormality of any kind is foreseen, the right to life is still his."

What do parents of retarded children think?

"There has not been a single organization of parents of mentally retarded children that has ever endorsed abortion. We, who are parents of these children and have borne the burden, ask that before you, the legislators, propose to speak for us, by possibly authorizing abortion for fetal abnormality, please ask our opinion first."

Mrs. Rosalie Craig, Testimony, Ohio Legislature, 1971

Have any courts ruled on this specific issue?

A major case came before the New Jersey Supreme Court in 1967, that of Gleitmen vs. Cosgrove. The parents had sued because the doctor had refused the mother an abortion after she had contracted rubella early in her pregnancy. Their suit was filed after the child had been born deformed. The court said:

"It is basic to the human condition to seek life and to hold on to it, however burdened. If Jeffrey could have been asked as to whether his life should be snuffed out before his full term of gestation could run its course, our felt intuition of human nature tells us he would almost surely choose life with defects as against no life at all.

"The right of life is inalienable in our society. A court cannot say what defects should prevent an embryo from being allowed life, such that denial of the opportunity to terminate the existence of the defective child in embryo can support a cause of action. The examples of famous persons who have had great achievements despite physical defects come readily to mind, and many of us can think of examples close to home. A child need not be perfect to have a worthwhile life.

"We are not faced with the necessity of balancing the mother's life against that of her child. The sanctity of the single human life is the decisive factor in this suit. Eugenic considerations are not controlling. We are not talking here about the breeding of prize cattle. It may have been easier for the mother, and less expensive for the father, to have terminated the life of their child while he was an embryo, but these detriments cannot stand against the preciousness of the single human life."

Why would abortion for deformity of the child be called pre-natal euthanasia?

Euthanasia, or mercy killing, generally refers to the active intervention in the normal course of a disease process, for a person who is incurably ill, and killing them. The word "mercy" relates to the fact that this person would presumably be killed only to prevent him from suffering needless pain and agony. Euthanasia, however, is broader than this, and in many people's interpretation, would include the 'puting away' of those who were hopelessly defective mentally, as well as those dying from physical disease. Both reasons for euthanasia have the same basic philosophy, i.e. because a life is no longer productive, comfortable, or useful, it is now all right to kill that person. This price tag of comfort or utilitarian usefulness, called euthanasia when applied to incurably ill post-born humans, applies equally well to the pre-born human who is also judged to be so deformed or mentally deficient that he too should not be permitted to live. This criteria and value judgment which permits humans to continue to live only because they are useful and independent is an utterly barbaric concept. Once life has a price tag on it and is no longer an absolute right, then all life is endangered, all life is only worth the current price tag placed upon it by society, the state, the master race, or those in positions of power.

> *"The fact that Germany has descended to the depths of Hitlerian mass murders does not immunize you (the U.S.A.) from the same human depravity."*
>
> Heinrich Pompey, M.D.
> Professor, University of Wurtzburg,
> Washington, D.C., October 1970

Is there that much difference between the concept of a "Master Race" (quality race) and the "quality life" of our modern pro-abortionist social planners?

Where could this philosophy lead?

Read THE WAITING ROOM.

THE

WAITING ROOM
2050 A.D.

BY DALE FRANCIS

When they had walked into the waiting room together, holding hands to give one another courage, the other people had looked at them and she felt a necessity to explain.

She sat there with her husband, looking around at the others in the room, then she turned to a man beside her, "My husband and I are exactly the same age, born the same day, that's how we happen to be here together."

The others looked at them, smiled, then turned inward to their own thoughts, having had the mystery solved.

One of the most terrible things about The Waiting Room was being there alone, without someone who loved you and cared about you. She thought to herself that she and Franklin were among the fortunate ones, the only ones who had the same birthdays of all the couples she knew. It was the second time in The Waiting Room for both of them. They were fifty-five.

The first time was the hardest of all. It was the dread of a new experience. Not that she doubted the wisdom of the government decision. There were too many people, everyone knew that, too many people. It was only reasonable to insist that people who did not contribute sufficiently to society should be — she hated to even think the words — be put to sleep.

The truth was the population hadn't really grown all that much. But, well, just as once a half century ago she and the boy who was to become her husband belonged to the youth majority, now they belonged to the elderly majority. It was as one of the senators had said, today's young people are too few to support a society that is predominately aged.

But fifty didn't seem at all old to her. She could understand why it was necessary to put all people more than 75 to sleep but fifty was only middle-aged. That was the age the government had decided on for the first of the Fives, though, and there was very little good that could come from arguing about it, one wouldn't want to be reported as uncooperative.

The first Five, when they were 50, was bad because it was first but it was rare that anyone failed the first Five, only the criminal elements, the drunkards, the disruptive, the uncooperative. The second Five was different, there were more who didn't make it and for lesser reasons.

That was why she worried about Franklin. He wasn't really doing very well at his job, he never had quite gotten used to the new computer equipment. His quality ratings hadn't been high, partly because Mr. Holden didn't seem to like him.

Ruth worried more about Frank than herself. She was a volunteer worker at the 24-hour-a-day child care center and she was good with children. One of the sadnesses of her life was that they had never had any children. There had been diabetes on Franklin's side of the family, that had meant they never were able to get a license to have a child. A child had been conceived but when she reported this to the doctor after six months, government officials placed her in the hospital. One of the nurses had told her the baby was a little girl. In her mind she had named her little girl Rita, her favorite name. Rita would have been 25 now. The irony was she would be needed now, the government no longer required abortions and young people were encouraged to have children but 30 years ago it was different. After the death of Rita — she never could think of it as anything but death although abortions were no more registered than appendectomies in those days—Franklin had been sterilized and she had been sterilized, too, it was one of the penalties for conceiving a child without a license.

A tall, military-looking man was called and he went into one of the examining rooms. He walked straight, his face set. He must have been 60.

She remembered the procedure. Three officials sat there, the record before them. They asked questions, more to perceive alertness than for the answers. One of her questioners had been a woman who was very kind to her, who spoke softly, comforting her in her nervousness. When the interview was finished the chairman of the committee nodded, either to the door behind them or to the door back to The Waiting Room. The woman had smiled and she knew they would point to The Waiting Room and they did.

A heavy-set woman was called, she looked as if she was only 50 and she laughed nervously and said, "Well, here goes nothing," speaking to no one in particular.

They called Ruth's name first. She held Franklin's hand. He had been sitting very quietly, his thin face set, there was the hint of tears in his eyes.

"It will be all right, Honey," she said.

There were two women and a man on the board, one of the women was the chairman. She looked at the record before her. "Are you nervous?" she asked. Ruth tried to speak but her mouth was dry and no words came out. She swallowed, "A little, I guess." "Your supervisor says you are excellent with children. Did you have children yourself?" Before Ruth could answer, the chairman said, "Oh, yes, I see. No children." Ruth thought of Rita again.

The man spoke, "I see you do not live at the center." Ruth answered quickly, "I live with my husband. But I never have missed a day's work, not one day in nearly 10 years. My husband sees that I'm always at the center on time."

They sat before her quietly. She knew they had already decided, they always had decided before you came in for one of the Fives. The chairman, who did not smile, spoke. "That will be all." She pointed to the door leading back to The Waiting Room. Ruth felt a surge of happiness, another five years, another five years.

She stepped back into The Wating Room. With a start she saw Franklin was not there. But of course, his name was called right after her own. The room was empty except for a man who had gone into committee room as she left it.

Franklin would be coming back soon. She sat down and waited for him. The time moved slowly. The man came back into The Waiting Room, smiling happily. She waited for Franklin. The clock on the wall moved so slowly. She continued to wait.

Then a brisk young woman came into The Waiting Room, saw her and looked surprised. "Were you waiting to be called before the committee?" she asked. "Oh, no," Ruth said. "I've been in. I'm waiting for Franklin, my husband, we have the same birthday, you know."

The young woman looked at her, sadly, almost as if she was going to cry, "I'm sorry," she said. "Everyone has gone. Perhaps your husband went on home." "Oh, yes," Ruth said. "Of course, he went on home ahead of me. Of course, that's what happened, he went on home ahead of me."

She left The Waiting Room. She would stop at the supermarket. She would buy shrimp, Franklin liked shrimp. What a dinner they would have, they would celebrate, another five years for both of them, they would celebrate.

She kept thinking of the celebration, allowing no other thoughts into her mind, right up to the moment she turned the lock on the door and stepped into the empty apartment.

14

RELIGION, VALUES,

HISTORY

Abortion was known and commonly practiced in the world of Greece and Rome into which Christianity came. Judaism, having developed a high respect for the family, for women, and for individual life, had condemned abortion but found certain exceptions to it. The Christian message brought a further dignity to the concept of the individual person and the value of his life. The idea of an individual, animate immortal soul given by God to every human person and hopefully returning to him for eternity, was a powerful concept which, within two centuries, transformed the Roman Empire. The value of the born person became associated closely with a similar value granted to the unborn person, and as Christian beliefs crystallized in writing and tradition, condemnation of abortion came to be, as Professor John T. Noonan of the University of California says in his book *"An almost absolute value."* (THE MORALITY OF ABORTION, Harvard University Press, 1970.)

The Gospel taught specifically that Jesus was conceived in Mary's womb by the Holy Spirit. What grew in her womb from conception was not a blob of protoplasm but the person of the God-man Jesus. Also clearly taught was that the infant John (the Baptist) ''leaped'' in the womb of Elizabeth. These specific references to the living personhood of the embryo were reinforced by the teachings of the

Fathers of the Church. The Didache said, *"You shall not slay the child by abortions."* Clement of Alexandria condemned abortion, as did Athenagoras: *"Those who use abortifacients are homicides."* Tertullian said, *"The mold in the womb may not be destroyed."* The Council of Ancyra in 314 denounced women who *"slay what is generated."* Another Council in 305 at Alvira excommunicated women committing abortion after adultery and would not even re-admit them to the Church at the point of death. While Sts. Jerome and Augustine questioned when the rational soul was given by God, this did not affect their complete moral condemnation of abortion. In the late fourth century, St. Basil wrote, *"The hair-splitting difference between formed and unformed makes no difference to us. Whoever deliberately commits abortion is subject to the penalty for homicide."*

By the time the curtain of the barbarian invasions rang down on the glory of Rome, the Christian teaching had codified itself into an extremely firm and certain moral opinion. Abortion was condemned. There was no question about Christian belief.

What was Thomas Aquinas's opinion 700 years later? The only specific reason Aquinas gave justifying an abortion was to bring out the growing baby so that it could be baptized. Thomas condemned abortion for any other reason. Interpretation of some of his thinking, however, has led some to assume that, if saving the life of the mother were the prime motive and action, and killing the baby a secondary effect, that this might have been permitted by Aquinas. This life-for-a-life ethic has been embodied in most of our state laws for over one-and-a-half centuries.

Aquinas also questioned whether human life began at conception. He spoke of the then-current scientific conviction that a male child was not fully enough developed to be judged human (and therefore to have a soul) until forty days, and that the female fetus could not be judged fully human until eighty days. This obviously says something about scientific knowledge of that age. Aquinas was reflecting a theological and scientific judgment that mirrored the most accurate scientific information of his time. When, to the most exact instrument available, the human eye, the unborn child looked like a child, it was deemed dignified and developed enough to be the possessor of an immortal soul, and so he made his conclusions.

Since that time, we have progressed to microscopes, to electron microscopes, to an increasingly sophisticated knowledge of chromosomes and genes. We now must make judgments in the light of our new and more accurate biological knowledge. Aquinas's conclusions were the best that could be expected in his day. While not applicable today they are of historical interest. Had men of his time had today's knowledge of embryonic and fetal development (see Chapter 4), their conclusions would have been different than what they were.

When did some changes in the earlier absolute Christian position begin to occur?

In the centuries before and after the Protestant Reformation, Christian thinkers came to debate and in some cases to justify the use of therapeutic abortion for the purpose of saving the life of the mother. Later, other reasons were added, such as the removal of an ectopic pregnancy (tubal pregnancy), or of a cancerous pregnant womb. Both of these killed the growing unborn child, but were not direct assaults upon the child's life for the purpose of destroying it. Rather, they had another more primary effect of saving the mother's life. No major religious bodies came to endorse abortion for less serious reasons until the twentieth century.

What is the Catholic position today?

The most authoritative statement in modern

times was made by the Second Vatican Council, which specifically said, *"Life from its conception is to be guarded with the greatest care. Abortion and infanticide are horrible crimes."* In contrast to its much more muted tone on contraception, which was directed to the "Children of the Church," the flat condemnation on abortion was directed to "All men of good will."

What do Orthodox Jews believe?

The official Orthodox Jewish position is an almost total condemnation of abortion. Rabbi Joseph Karisick, President of the Union of Jewish Orthodox Congregations of America, and Rabbi Bernard Berzon, President of the Rabbinical Council in America said that to terminate a pregnancy for arbitrary reasons was *"literally for man to play God and is religiously blasphemous and socially destructive."* No woman is the *"final arbiter of the disposition of her body and the embryonic human life flourishing therein."*

What of the Mormon Church?

Joseph Smith, President of the Mormon Church, said, *"The destruction of life, even thought of as a fetus, is contrary to the whole concept of Christian living."*

What of Reformed Judaism?

Opinions vary, but perhaps a general statement that Reformed Jews are permissive on abortions would be reasonably accurate.

Aren't most people who oppose abortion Catholics?

Definitely not. The state of Washington is only 12% Catholic. Recently, a permissive law was passed, but 46% of the voters voted against it.

One of the reasons that many people feel that most opposition to abortion is from Catholics is that almost one-fourth of the people of the nation are Catholic, many of whom do oppose abortion, and their opposition looms large. If, for example, one-fourth of the nation were Orthodox Jews, or were Mormons, they probably would be thought of as the main force against abortion.

The pro-abortionists have, incidentally, tried hard and at times fairly successfully to label all who oppose them as Catholic.

Aren't all Catholics subservient to the directives of their Church?

Definitely not. As everyone knows, a large percentage of "good" Catholics disagree with their church's laws on birth control. In fact, most Catholics who oppose abortion do so not because the church tells them to but because they are convinced that the unborn child is human and should be protected.

What of Catholics who are public officials?

Equally permissive laws were passed in 1970 in Hawaii, Alaska, and Maryland. Hawaii's Catholic Governor Burns did not veto the bill there, which became law. Maryland's Governor Mandel, a Jew, vetoed Maryland's law, which killed the bill. Alaska's Methodist Governor Miller vetoed his state's law, which was passed over his veto.

Isn't it true that Roman Catholic Church's complete condemnation of abortion dates only from 1869?

Absolutely not! The only aspect that has been subject to debate in the Catholic Church has been the time of ensoulment. Abortion, whether a soul has been judged present or not, has always been flatly condemned.

What is the Lutheran thinking about abortion?

Four great Lutheran theologians come to mind. Karl Barth said, *"He who destroys germinating life kills a man."* Deitrich Bonhoffer said, *"To raise the question whether we are here concerned already with a human being or not is merely to confuse the issue. The simple fact is that God certainly intended to create a human being and that this nascent human being has been deliberately deprived of his life and that is nothing but murder."* Professor Otto Piper of Princeton has stated that, *"We have no right to destroy new life."* Professor Helmut Thielicke, Professor of Religion at the University of Hamburg, specifically states, *"Once impregnation has taken place it is no longer a question of whether the persons concerned have the responsibility for a possible parenthood. They have become parents."*

Are there other prominent Protestant theologians who oppose abortion?

Among the many who have spoken, Dr. Paul Ramsey, Professor of the School of Divinity at Princeton has said that, *"There is more than one patient in the case of abortion."* and has spoken of the incongruity of doctors trained to save lives now destroying them. Dr. Herbert Richardson of the Harvard School of Divinity shares this thinking. Dr. Norman Vincent Peale is also opposed to abortion.

What of the Greek Orthodox Church?

They are completely opposed to abortion.

Which religions groups are pro-abortion?

A high percent of Secular Humanists are pro-abortion. Many Unitarians, Reformed Jews, and some Methodists, Presbyterians, and other orthodox Protestant people favor abortion. Generally speaking, only

a small minority of Baptists and the more funda-
mentalist oriented Christian Churches favor abortion.

Can you tell from a person's religion, then, what his opinion about abortion will be?

As you can see from the above, there are all varieties of opinions in all of the Churches. Certain dominant convictions, however, are evident in some.

Are any minds being changed?

Certainly yes. The almost total emphasis and publicity given in recent years to the mother's problems has slowly been shifting many sincere religious people's convictions toward permitting abortion. When, however, they are given a full exposure to the facts such as contained in this book, most people return to their original conviction, that the unborn child has a basic right to life that can only be revoked for extremely serious reasons.

15

LEGAL RIGHTS OF

THE CHILD

"We hold these truths to be self-evident; that all men are created equal, that they are endowed by their Creator with certain unalienable rights, that among these rights are life . . .
. . that to secure these rights, governments are instituted among men . . ."

Declaration of Independence

"Nor shall any state deprive any person of life, liberty, or property without due process of law, nor deny to any person within its jurisdiction that equal protection of the laws."

14th Amendment, Constitution of the U.S.

"The child, by reason of his physical and mental immaturity, needs special safeguards and care, including appropriate legal protection, before as well as after birth."

Declaration of the Rights of a Child
General Assembly of the United Nations
November 20, 1959

Almost without exception, every state, soon after it was admitted to the Union, came to put a law on its books regarding abortion. Worded in different ways, sometimes in even vague or unscientific terms, the meaning of these laws remained entirely clear to every one until the present decade. They simply meant that abortion was a crime and was forbidden by the laws of the state unless it was necessary to preserve the life of the mother. No other indications were recognized, except a varience of the above which spoke of serious threat to her physical health or life. In the past decade, the laws of many states have been challenged in the courts. Some of these original laws have been ruled unconstitutional by state or district federal courts. Just as many have been upheld as constitutional, and remain the law of that state. Many reasons have been given by the various courts, state and federal, for the decisions granted.

The major paradox within the legal community in modern times has been the rapid acceptance of the rights of the unborn child to all sorts of legal protection, safeguards, and redress from harm. In the face of this has come an increasing permissiveness by some courts and state legislatures to deny the unborn child the most basic right of all, the right to life.

In 1965, the Supreme Court of the United States recognized the right of marital privacy in voiding a law preventing the dissemination of contraceptive devices (Griswold v. Connecticutt). Some courts have extended this "right of privacy" to allow abortion. What do you think?

The best answer to this recently was given by the federal judges in the United States District Court, Northern District of Ohio, January 1971:

> *"This court . . . believes that the cases that do accept (this association) have not been based on a proper legal factual understanding. The plaintiff's contentions seek to extend far beyond the holdings in the Griswold case this 'right of privacy,' which is nowhere expressly mentioned in the constitution or its amendments, but is*

95

found only in the 'penumbra' of those articles. Rights, the provision of which is only implied or deduced, must inevitably fall in conflict with the express provisions of the Fifth and Fourteenth Amendments that no person should be deprived of life without due process of law. The difference between this case and Griswold is clearly apparent for here there is an embryo or fetus incapable of defending itself. There the only lives are those of the two competent adults.

"Without going into all of the myriad of cases and texts that deal with various aspects of this problem, the question resolves itself into whether the state has a legitimate interest to legislate for the purpose of affording an embryonic or fetal organism an opportunity to survive. We think it has, and on balance it is superior to the claimed right of a pregnant woman, or anyone else to destroy the fetus except when necessary to preserve her own life."

(See also Chapter 8)

How long has an unborn child had the right of inheritance?

As early as 1795 in Doe v. Clarke (2H. Bl. 399, 126 Eng. Rep. 617), the court interpreted the ordinary meaning of the word "children" in a will to include a child in the womb. The court: "An infant (in the womb) who by the course and order of nature is then living, comes clearly within the description of 'children living' at the time of the decease (of the person who made the will).

Further, in 1798, in Thelluson v. Woodford (4 Ves. 277, 31 Eng. Rep. 117), the court said that unborn children are "entitled to all the privileges of other persons."

Several other decisions might be mentioned, including a one in 1927 where a trust fund originating from the estate of the deceased was to be divided into "as many parts as I have grandchildren living at the date of my decease". The person willing the property died on May 22, 1922. A granddaughter of the deceased was conceived on May 1, 1922. The court (Swain v. Bowers, 91, Ind. 307, N.E. 598, 1927) ruled that the granddaughter was entitled to a share in the estate.

But didn't Justice Oliver Wendell Holmes in 1884 rule that an unborn baby was "not a person" in the eyes of the law? (Deitrich v. Northhampton).

This is true but Professor William Prosser, author of The Law of Torts (third edition) states that the reversal of the Deitrich doctrine *"has been sweeping."* Practically every jurisdiction that has considered the issue in the last generation has upheld the right of an infant to sue for injuries prior to birth.

Can a child sue for injuries prior to birth?

This also, as Professor W. Prosser above has written, has become a completely accepted practice in our time. Children injured in the Thalidomide tragedy, some of them from pills taken as early as two to three weeks after conception, have consistently won court decisions granting them sums of money for their support because of the deformities they suffered from the drug while in the uterus.

Injuries received by an unborn child in its mother's womb from auto accidents have been fairly common and recoveries have been consistently granted.

But these were only granted to the children after they were born, not while yet unborn.

True to an extent. At first, awards were limited to those cases in which the child was born alive, and either died from injuries or remained alive with some handicap. More significant, however, has been a more recent trend allowing the parents or survivors to institute such an action even when the child is stillborn. Therefore, an unborn child, who dies within the womb as a result of an accident, and who never experiences life outside of the womb has still been held to be "a person" who can sue for damages because of his death (Louisell, "Abortion, the Practice of Medicine and the Due Process of Law," 16, UCLA Law Rev. 233, 1969.)

Give an example.

The Massachusetts Supreme Court in April of 1927 (Torrigan v. Watertown News Co., 352 Mass. 446, 225 N.E. 2nd 926, 1967) in allowing recovery of damages for the wrongful death following prenatal injury said: *"In the vast majority of cases where the present issue has arisen, recovery has been allowed . . . To the extent that the views of text writers and legal commentators have come to our attention, they are unanimously of the view that non-viability of a fetus should not bar recovery."*

It further held that the unborn child was a *"person"* in the eyes of the law.

I've heard an unborn child can get social security benefits. Is this true?

A recent decision by the U.S. Court of Appeals for the Fifth Circuit (1969) verified this. The father of an illegitimate child was killed a short time after the child was conceived. The right of the child to receive social security benefits on the earning record of the father depended on whether the father was "living with" the child at the time he died. The court held that the unborn child was living with the father at that time, and said: *"Medically speaking, Donna was viable from the instant of conception onward. An action for damages would have been brought in her*

behalf for injuries she might have received prior to birth.
When the deceased wage earner came over for his weekend
visits, he was in fact living with both child and mother."
(Wagner v. Gardner, 413 F2d 267)

In 1970, the state laws forbidding abortion were declared
unconstitutional in California, Texas, Wisconsin and Wash.
D.C. Isn't this a major trend?

These have been well publicized, but few people
realize that more states in that very same year,
considering laws that were essentially similar, upheld
the constitutionality of those laws. This was true for
the Louisiana Supreme Court, (State v. Pesson 235 So.
2d 568, 1970), the Iowa Supreme Court (State v.
Abodelly, docket #66, crosshatch 53864, 1970), and the
Vermont Supreme Court. It was also true for trial
courts in two states, including the Massachusetts case
of Commonwealth v. Brunelle which said specifically
that, *"The evidence before me clearly establishes that*
the product of human conception, whether it be in the
state of zygote, embryo, or fetus, may properly be clas-
sified as human life." A Minesota State Court, re-
fusing to dismiss a criminal abortion indictment (State
v. Hodgson, Minn., 2nd judicial district, file #23789,
1970) said: *"It would appear that the time has been*
reached when society must discard the theory advanced
by the old Roman law, that the parent has absolute
dominion over his offspring, or a return to the ancient
notion that a fetus is a 'part' of his mother."

The Ohio Federal Court mentioned above, in de-
claring the Ohio law also constitutional, said: *"The legal*
conclusions in Griswold as to the rights of individuals
to determine without governmental interference whether
or not to enter into the process of procreation cannot be
extended to cover those situations wherein, voluntarily
or involuntarily, the preliminaries have ended and a new
life has begun. Once human life has commenced, the
Constitutional protections found in the Fifth and Four-
teenth Amendments impose on the state the duty of
safeguarding it."

The U.S. Supreme Court has since (Apr. '71) ruled that the Wisconsin and Wash. D.C. laws are, in fact, constitutional, overturning the lower court decisions.

What if a doctor refuses to abort a mother. Can he be sued?

Such a case came before the New Jersey Supreme Court (Gleitman v. Cosgrove, 1967). The parents had sued because the doctor refused the mother an abortion after she had contracted rubella. The child was born deformed. The parents sued in his behalf for damages because the doctor had not aborted him. The court said:

> *"It is basic to the human condition to seek life and to hold on to it however burdened. If Jeffrey could have been asked as to whether his life should be snuffed out before his full term of gestation had run its course, our felt intuition of human nature tells us he would almost certainly choose life with defects as against no life at all.*

> *"The right of life is inalienable in our society. A court cannot say what defects should prevent an embryo from being allowed life . . . Examples of famous persons who have had great achievements despite physical defects come readily to mind, and many of us can think of examples close to home. A child need not be perfect to have a worthwhile life.*

> *"We are not faced with the necessity of balancing a mother's life against that of her child. The sanctity of the single human life is the decisive factor in the case . . . It may have been easier for the mother and less expensive for the father to have terminated the life of their child while he was an embryo, but these detriments cannot stand against the preciousness of the single human life."*

Have there been many decisions supporting the right of the unborn child before he is "viable"?

The Supreme Court of South Carolina (Fowler v. Woodward 148 S.E. 2d 142, 1964), specifically held that an action for wrongful death on behalf of a stillborn child could be maintained in that state and noted that "a slight majority" of American jurisdictions allow the maintenance of such a cause. Judge Haynsworth spoke forcefully to this matter: *"It seems to me evident that limiting recovery in these cases to injuries suffered after the child becomes viable is a social perversion without support in reason or historical precedents. Viability of the child at the time of injury ought to be recognized as the imposter it is and sheared of all future influence upon our judgments."* (341 F. 2d at 79)

Have there been any cases of an unborn child suing even before his birth?

Recent advances in the medical science of fetology have made it possible to treat the "littlest patient" prior to birth. One such new advance is the possibility of giving a blood transfusion to a baby while yet in his mother's uterus who would otherwise die because of an Rh problem. In just such a case, the child's mother, a member of a religious sect forbidding blood transfusion, refused to allow an intra-uterine blood transfusion for her unborn child. She objected to the invasion of her own body, stated she had a right to "privacy", and also that this violated a firmly held religious conviction of hers. The New Jersey Supreme Court (Fitkin v. Anderson 42 N.J. 421, 201 A. 2d 537, 1964) noted that her right to freely practice religious belief was one of the most fundamental and sacred constitutional rights, and that her right to her own body was also a basic right. It clearly decided, however, that this right would have to be subordinated to the unborn child's right to survival, which it stated, was a value outweighing the parent's constitutional right to practice in this manner her religious beliefs.

The state can take a life in levying capital punishment. What difference is this from allowing abortion?

There are two major differences. First, the life that the state takes is judged a guilty one, whereas the unborn child is totally innocent. Second, the life taken by the state is done so after due process of law and adequate hearings pro and con. Abortion laws totally ignore due process of law.

So far you have only discussed legal decisions which uphold the rights of the unborn child as a human person. Other decisions have denied him this right, have they not?

This is true. We believe, however, that the decisions in favor of the unborn child constitute a clear trend. Few people know of them. Our purpose is to bring these decisions to people's attention, as the anti-life decisions have usually received their full share of publicity.

What other rights does the unborn child have legally?

He can have a guardian appointed, can ask for an injunction, and may be an executor.

Isn't this, then, a mixed-up mess?

In answer and conclusion, let us quote from "The Rights of the Unborn at Law" by Martin McKernen, Jr. and Michael Taylor, 1970:

> *"Recent legislative and judicial developments in regard to abortion have created an alarming legal phenomena. Neither the proponents of abortion-on-demand nor the American Law Institute's Model Penal Code have taken into consideration the procedural safeguards which every other area of the law throws up around the rights of the unborn child. There is a contradiction inherent in*

a legal system which will allow the institution of a wrongful death action for the death of an unborn child through the actions of a negligent party and yet, at the same time, permit that child's parents to effect his death because he poses a threat to the mental health of the mother, or presents an inconvenience to the family. A cursory examination of the recent abortion proposals clearly indicates that they stand in direct contradiction to fundamental principles of the American legal system. There is no basis in law or in logic for a measure which would allow the destruction without due process of law, of a being which every other area of the legal spectrum recognizes as a human being.

"Discussion has centered about the rights of the mother, the rights of the family, or the rights of society when speaking of abortion. Little, however, has been said in regards to the rights of that being most directly affected, the unborn child. Fundamental to all the other rights which the law has bestowed upon the unborn child is the right to life — — and without this one, all of the others are meaningless. A legal system which places two such principles in such total contradiction cannot properly be called a system at all."

16

THE POOR SUFFER

A constantly repeated reason to justify abortion-on-demand is that present restrictive laws discriminate against the poor. It is stated that those with money can, in one way or another, obtain abortions if they really want them and that the poor simply cannot.

Isn't it true that restrictive abortion laws are unfair to the poor?

It is probably true that it is safer for a rich person to break almost any law, than for a poor person to do so. Perhaps the poor cannot afford all the heroin they want. Rich people probably can. Does that mean we should make heroin available to everyone? Not everything that money can buy is necessarily good. The solution is not to repeal laws, but to enforce them fairly. Laws restricting abortion can be, and frequently have been, adequately enforced.

But it's still basically unfair, isn't it?

What is unfair is that poor people have not been given an adequate education and an adequate opportunity to better themselves. We will not eliminate poverty by killing poor people. The problem of the poor and the under-educated is their destitution and their lack of opportunity to achieve a better life, not the fact that they have children. Some who live in ivory towers seem unaware of this, but poor people themselves are very much aware of it, as evidenced by the fact that they as a group have cut their birth rate much less than middle and upper class socio-economic groups. (p. 57)

But don't too many children add to the burden of their poverty?

Poverty is more than just a shortage of this world's goods. Poverty is also the lack of spiritual and cultural resources, and often accompanying it is despair, apathy, and helplessness. Those who lack material things, and often find their chances for improvement of their lot in life rather bleak, sometimes find that much of their personal fulfillment is the joy they find in their children.

Do poor people tend not to accept abortion?

The majority certainly have not up until this time. Neither have poor or under-developed or under-educated areas of the world in any significant numbers accepted methods of birth control. It is the middle and upper classes who have accepted and used these methods.

What is the answer then for the poor?

The humane solution is to attempt to raise their standard of living and to help them achieve a more dignified existence. By raising a family's expectations in life, and the degree of education which they hope their children will achieve, people have universally been motivated to limit the number of children they have, in order to take adequate care of those children they have already borne. This seems to be the only way that will consistently motivate people to voluntarily limit their family size.

Are these white people, black people, Indians? Of whom do you speak?

We speak of them all, particularly however non-white people throughout the world who suspect that the imposition of birth control and abortion on their cultures is the white man's method of genocide.

Genocide? Who said this?

In April, 1971, Mr. Wm. Darity, head of the Dept. of Public Health, Univ. of Mass. speaking at a Planned Parenthood Conference in Kansas City about his STUDY OF A NEW ENGLAND COMMUNITY said that:

"The study found parallel increasing evidence of strong opposition to family planning among blacks, including such moderate black civil rights organizations as the Southern Christian Leadership Conference.

"Considerably more black males under 30 agreed that family planning programs were designed to eliminate blacks." Also they were *"Overwhelmingly opposed to sterilization and abortion, 'even if you had all the children you wanted' ".*

17

WHAT DOCTORS THINK

"Physicians are not sociologists, nor theologians, nor economists. We do not judge the quality of life. We are simply healers. Any act on the part of a physician contrary to the preservation of life stands as a position hopelessly contrary to the tradition of Hippocratic medicine.

"I extend this cautionary observation to today's abortion enthusiasts. Unwanted pregnancy may be indeed a social problem, but it is not an illness. If we as physicians are to treat social or other non-medical problems, our patients will not be too long in realizing that we have abandoned the ancient and sacred role of healer. They will be surely right in viewing us then as any other purveyor of a service, another merchant."

A.M.A. News, Dr. Bestler

Is the A.M.A. really in favor of abortions?

The American Medical Association's House of Delegates has been involved for the last several years in the most bitter arguments that have ever come to the floor of the A.M.A. To say that there is a concensus of opinion would be a wild exaggeration. There is a deep disagreement between members of the A.M.A. on the question of abortion. All that has been voted on approvingly by that House of Delegates is a rather carefully worded document which, in so many words, says that a doctor may do what the state law says is legal. Whether this policy will continue or will be changed next year is anybody's guess.

How have doctors reacted to this new policy?

This tentative policy has been deeply divisive. Some physicians have already resigned from the A.M.A. over this issue but most have remained as members and are working toward re-establishing the policy of respect for life upon which medicine is founded.

It is not unreasonable to predict that if its official policy would permanently become pro-abortion, the A.M.A. would lose a significant segment of its membership. If this happens it would lose its effectiveness as a unified voice of American medicine, as other medical organizations of differing philosophies would grow in size and influence.

Are there other medical organizations?

Yes, there are several. One that has recently spoken said this:

"Be it resolved that the Assembly and House of Delegates of the Association of American Physicians and Surgeons, Inc. in regular session assembled in Richmond, Va., this 3rd day of October, 1970, condemn and oppose indiscriminate liberalization of the indications for abortion which will permit abortion on demand."

Has the A.M.A. spoken about any restrictions?

On December 19, 1970, Mr. Bernard Hersh, head of the A.M.A. Legal Dept., said that the A.M.A. was "violently opposed" to abortions in advanced stages of pregnancy as is now permitted in New

York. He said that this was in opposition to the A.M.A.'s policy on medical practice, and said that most doctors, from a medical point of view, feel it is unwise to abort a woman after twelve or fourteen weeks.

Reacting to the just-reported news that 26 babies had been aborted alive in New York, one of them having eventually been adopted into a family, he said that he was "horrified" at the news, and hoped that the New York law would be changed: *"I think live abortion is an evil thing. Anyone in his right mind would say that it is horrible."*
(Ed. note: All babies are alive before abortion. Abortion kills them.)

Has the A.M.A. spoken further about abortion?

At the same meeting, the A.M.A. flatly condemned the abortion mills that have sprung up in New York, and the solicitations being made by New York doctors in these abortion mills. *"We want to make it loud and clear to these hucksters in abortion that this practice is unethical and it is condemned by the medical profession."*

Is there a trend in what doctors think about abortion? Are there any accurate studies of this?

In America, most of the polls taken merely reflect what doctors think they're going to be feeling about abortion, and do not reflect much actual experience. There definitely does seem to be a trend away from further liberalization now that the New York situation has exposed to all some of the things that happen with an abortion-on-demand permissiveness. All that can be said at the moment is that it is a hotly debated subject, and no person could say that "doctors' are convinced one way or another.

But don't you have some feel for doctors' opinions here?

The thrust of feeling seems to us quite universal. There is a small minority, possibly 5% or less of physicians, who would favor no bars at all to unlimited abortion. There is a strong minority, perhaps 20-30% or more of doctors who would oppose abortion under any circumstance except to save the life of the mother. There is that large mid-group which includes physicians who would allow an abortion, but only for limited reasons.

It is totally meaningless to simply ask physicians or any other group if they are in favor of abortion or not. There are so many qualifications, if's, and but's, that you must separate these replies into a series of categories of permissiveness.

If the U.S. has no real opinion formulated yet, what of other countries like England?

England has had a wide-open abortion law for several years. Recently, all the consultants of the Royal College of Obstetrics and Gynecology were polled in depth as to their opinions about abortion. The results, published in the British Medical Journal, May 1970, were most interesting.

"Do you favor abortion-on-demand?"

No	--	92%
Yes	--	4%
No answer	--	4%

Eighty percent felt that, if abortions were performed, that they should be done only by a consultant gynecologist and in a hospital, but only 21% of the doctors were willing to actually do any of the abortions themselves.

Of the physicians doing abortions, 75% had encountered opposition, from their nursing staffs, to their performing abortions. (It is interesting that Britain is less than 10% Catholic.)

Two-thirds of the gynecologists felt that the fact of their performing abortions would cut down on the number of young physicians interested in entering their specialty.

Other problems were mentioned, including two instances in which the admission of women subsequently found to have female cancer was delayed several months because abortion cases had been given priority.

Only 4% of British gynecologists now favor abortion-on-demand?

Yes. This was a point of great annoyance to the Royal College, which spoke of it several times, specifically: *"When the abortion bill was under discussion, its advocates repeatedly assured the Houses of Parliament that abortion-on-demand was not their object. Had they done otherwise, it is unlikely that the bill would have become law. Once the bill was passed, however, there has been a persistent and intense campaign which has had the effect of making the public believe that any woman has a right to have a pregnancy terminated if she so wishes."*

What is the motivation of the minority of doctors who are in favor of abortion-on-demand?

Unquestionably, many of the physicians who expouse this view are sincere people who do it for idealistic reasons.

Unquestionably also, a fair percentage of those who are pushing hard for this are going to financially exploit it to the limit. Dr. Vincent O'Sullivan, honorary

111

consultant to the crown in London, has stated flatly that an abortion in England is available if a woman wants it and if the doctor is well paid. He has suggested an amendment to the law that would require listing the medical indications for an abortion, and insisting that there be no financial gain to either the doctor or the hospital.

You mean doctors would do these just to make money?

Certainly, not most physicians, but unquestionably, there would be a small number who would abuse this in the most blatant fashion. Where vast sums of money are involved, the temptation for some would be too great. In a recent issue of Medical Economics, (November 23, 1970, "Suddenly I'm a Legal Abortionist",) a physician, describing his experience in doing abortions in New York said: *"Financially, after years of struggle, I can't help feeling a little like the Texan who drilled for water and struck oil."*

In a subsequent issue (Medical Economics, Jan. 4, 1971, The Wild Scramble for Abortion Money) a prominent obstetrician relates how he was approached to lend his name and prestige to a small private hospital set up specifically to perform abortions: *"A syndicate invited me to be its medical director for up to $250,000 a year".*

In what other ways is money made from abortions?

In a New York State Health Committee hearing in March, 1971, Senator Tarky Lombardi from Syracuse described a New York City abortion referral agency which, since July, 1970, had already paid a $64,000 dividend on a $1,000 investment.
(A. M. A. News, March 15, 1970.)

In short, you don't think that a majority of physicians in the United States are in favor of any substantial liberalization of abortion laws?

That is correct.

Is it true that actual experimentation has been done on aborted human fetuses?

As can be seen in Fig. VIII, this is a fact. Nothing more need be said.

This could never happen in America.

Your authors have personal testimony of eye witnesses that live aborted babies delivered by hysterotomy in a major U.S. teaching hospital were put on ice and quickly taken to a university laboratory for experimentation, before being killed.

What do most doctors think of this sort of thing?

It cannot be stated strongly enough that the overwhelming majority view this sort of activity as revolting, subhuman, barbaric, and disgusting and would catagorically condemn it. When however, the door to abortion-on-demand is opened, things like this are bound to happen. Once reverence for life is lost at any stage of human life, appalling practices like this abuse soon appear.

What do nurses think?

Nurses, probably far more than physicians, have been upset by and have rebelled against abortion. In a poll of nurses published in the June, 1970 issue of R.N. Magazine, the following opposed unrestricted abortion:

Operating Room Nurses	87%
Delivery Room Nurses	85%
Intensive Care Nurses	83%
General Duty Nurses	82%
Pediatric Nurses	77%
Administrative Nurses	74%
Psychiatric Nurses	69%
Emergency Room Nurses	64%

Human Experimentation

THE LAST HOURS OF AN ABORTED BABY. Dr. Lawrence Lawn, of Cambridge University's Department of Experimental Medicine at work experimenting on a living, legally aborted, human fetus. Some British doctors have been vigorously defending their experiments on live aborted babies after a storm of protest blew up in England when a Member of Parliament told the press that private abortion clinics had been selling live aborted babies for research. Dr. Lawn was quoted in the Cambridge Evening News as saying "We are simply using something which is destined for the incinerator to benefit mankind ... Of course we would not dream of experimenting with a viable child. We

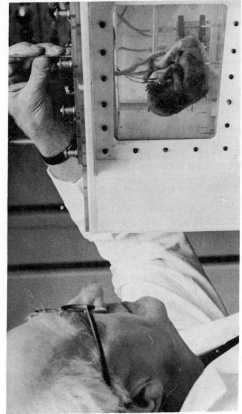

would not consider that to be right". The Langham Street (abortion) Clinic, admitted sending aborted fetuses to the Middlesex Hospital (The People, May 17, 1970). A spokesman for the clinic said that the fetuses 'were aged between eighteen and twenty-two weeks ... Our doctor had to give some special attention to the operation. He did this at his own expense and dispatched the fetuses to his colleague at the Middlesex Hospital. It had to be done pretty promptly, but the hospital is only a couple of minutes away.' In the News of the World, for the same date, this same man, Mr. Philip Stanley, is also quoted as saying "The position is quite clear. A fetus has to be 28 weeks to become legally viable. Earlier than that it is so much garbage".

Fig. VIII (with permission, Minnesota Citizens Concerned for Life)

114

WHAT HAPPENS TO THOSE WHO KILL?

"What happens to a man who lets the blood of another man? This is the real question, the tragic question. The question of bloodletting is not, from the point of view of tragic vision, interesting at all. But the question of consequences, of psychic change, of the corruption of man's spirit, this is very nearly the only question worth asking" . . . . .

What happens in the heads of those who accede to bloodletting as a social method? What happens to the social managers, to the intellectuals, to the actionists, to the students when men turn toward death as a way of life."

No Bars To Manhood, by Dan Berrigan, 1970

(Editors note: The above was written about war. We believe it applies equally well to abortion.)

"Acts of great evil come easily to human nature. All that man's malleable conscience demands is a heroically articulated excuse combined with the comradeship of other evil-doers. In other words, if the end is seen as both important and virtuous, then any means will often do. And the burden of solitary guilt need not be born if great numbers are also practicing the obscenity.

It is easier for a man to kill if those around him are killing, and it is easier for a man to kill if he has killed before. All fanatical tyrants have known this, from ancient oriental chieftans to Torquemada to Hitler to Mao. The moral instincts of humans are generally fragile, and if they are not constantly renewed by vigorous use, they wear away until they crumble completely.

Edwin A. Roberts, National Observer, Jan. 18, 1971

"She had a number tattooed on her arm when I examined her. The origin of the tattoo was obvious and familiar — Buchenwald. I asked her if she would like to have it removed by plastic surgery, but she declined. She said she would wear it to her grave, for it was her diploma from the school of life. "Doctor, I don't know where you learned what life is, but I know where I learned it. I don't even step on cockroaches now."

James J. Diamond, M.D., America, July 19, 1969

PART III

ACTION

18

CORRECT SOCIAL

INJUSTICE

Books have been written on this subject, and its many aspects. Space does not permit any major investigation or lengthy commentary here. Let this not, however, give our readers any false impression. Correcting social injustice is, without question, the most important aspect of the entire abortion problem. Women want abortions because, in the vast majority of situations, they are in social or economic difficulties. To merely oppose abortion and do no more is not only useless, but frankly immoral. Anyone active in the pro-life movement should be equally as active in a wide variety of social actions.

Basic to the entire problem is the fragmentation of family life in this century. Anything that can be done to help restore the dignity and security of family life will go a long way toward eliminating the problems that seem to call for abortion. To restore the dignity of women and the masculinity of men is of utmost importance. To accept our human sexuality, joyfully, but also responsibly, is the job that is cut out for each of us. That we should work for racial justice should go without saying. Positive actions such as those of Birthright should be implemented immediately. Responsible family planning is essential. So many other social wrongs cry for our attention. e.g. the billions being spent on bombs instead of people, the polluting of our planet, the outrage of our prisons, the abuse of some of our courts and legal processes rendering justice at times so difficult to come by -- all of these and others are important. No one person can apply himself to them all. Our world needs each person's best efforts, with the responsibility resting heavily on Americans who have been given such a big share of this world's gifts. Each can take different points of departure and try to make this world a little better place than the world each of us came into.

The problem of abortion, we believe, rates absolute top priority in the field of human problems that we have mentioned. It does so not simply because it is, in many ways, related to the problems above, but because, if permissive abortion becomes the practice of our country, this fact itself will go a long way toward making many of the above problems worse. It would seem at first glance to some people that to kill off your problems eliminates the problems. In the long run, however, the philosophy of disrespect for human life that this entails erodes the very foundation stone of a stable society, and ultimately will cause far greater chaos and human misery than the somewhat easy solution it may present to some on the surface.

19

FAMILY PLANNING

Among the positive alternatives that must be discussed, family planning ranks very high. Few today argue against responsible family planning. It has come to be an accepted value in our culture, endorsed as such by most concerned people and religious bodies. To say that a married couple should attempt to have only as many children as they can adequately care for is to repeat a self-evident norm, a norm that we would agree with completely.

Family planning, we are convinced, is the right and duty of each couple themselves. No one, most specifically the state, has the right to tell parents (much less to enforce) how many children a family should or should not have.

The method used for limitation of conceptions is, as we all know, controversial. This relates back again to the individual moral beliefs, ethics, tastes, financial resources, etc., of the people involved. Any specific couple has the right to use whichever method is acceptable and best for them.

What about sterilization?

For our purposes, we would usually point out that surgical sterilization is in essence a permanent form of contraception. Whether or not this would be an acceptable method would again depend upon a person's moral convictions, their social and economic situation, their psychological stability, and many personal reasons. Sterilization, while a permanent mutilation of a body faculty, is something immensely less damaging to the moral fiber of a civilization than killing the human life already living within a mother's uterus.

What about compulsory sterilization for those who have major, dominant genetic defects which they would be passing on to their children?

Conscientious people with a hereditary defect would be well-advised to refrain from having their own children, but rather to adopt other children as their own if they desire a family. Compulsory sterilization for some such reasons has already been enacted into the law in some states. Not many would agree with this type of law and activity. Even this, however, is something essentially less than the deliberate taking of a human life once conceived, since this involves only that person's body and not the life of another human being as abortion does.

But family planning methods don't always work. What happens if a woman becomes pregnant and didn't want to be?

Over a lifetime, statistically speaking, most family planning methods do work. They also do fail in individual situations. Many people who are reading these words have been surprised by an unplanned pregnancy. Most of these originally unplanned pregnancies over a period of nine months, however, came to be wanted and after birth became very cherished and loved children indeed. Truly, family planning, while not always "working" in each individual instance will, if averaged out over a lifetime of marriage, in almost all cases be very effective indeed in producing a family of approximately the size that a particular couple would desire.

Isn't abortion just another method of birth control?

Definitely not. Birth control attempts to prevent a new life from beginning. Abortion kills the life of the human person already conceived. There is a vast difference. In many peoples' minds, the one is quite acceptable while the other is totally rejected.

One remains the personal decision of the couple. The other involves a society's responsibility in safeguarding another person's life.

What has Planned Parenthood said?

The following is a quote from an official Planned Parenthood pamphlet published in August, 1963.

"Is birth control an abortion?

Definitely not. An abortion kills the life of a baby after it has begun. It is dangerous to your life and health. It may make you sterile so that when you want a child you cannot have it. Birth control merely postpones the beginning of life."

As most people are aware, in many large cities Planned Parenthood is now in the forefront of those urging permissive abortion laws and helping pregnant women find physicians who will *"kill the life of a baby after it has begun."*   (quote above).

20

BIRTHRIGHT

This ad appeared in the student newspaper of a major midwestern university.

ABORTION COUNSELING, INFORMATION AND REFERRAL SERVICES

Abortions up to 24 weeks of pregnancy are now legal in New York State. There are no residency restrictions at cooperating hospitals and clinics. Only the consent of the patient and the performing physician is required.

If you think you are pregnant, consult your doctor. Don't delay. Early abortions are simpler and safer.

If you need information or professional assistance, including immediate registration into available hospitals and clinics, telephone:

THE ABORTION ██████ INC.

██████ STREET
NEW YORK, N. Y. ███

The following week this ''ad'' appeared.

We are adoptive parents. Our children were given the gift of life by men and women other than ourselves. Our children live now because these women and men chose life instead of death. We can never comprehend the suffering they endured. But we shall always be thankful for their courage and generosity. Their gift of life shall flourish.

— A ██████ faculty member and wife

Which choice will the pregnant girl make? Death to the living one within her? Or will she give the child life?

Most mothers, if given help, will choose life. The problem is that society often gives her little alternative to abortion. For a variety of reasons, women have often not asked for help from existing agencies or have feared disclosure or red tape if they went to them. Now private groups have been formed to aid in obtaining abortions. What is needed is help for the distraught mother who isn't sure she wants an abortion.

In the face of this need, Birthright has appeared.

What is Birthright?

Birthright, founded by **Mrs.** Louise Summerhill in Toronto, Canada, in October, 1968, has the creed: *"The right of every mother to give birth; the right of every child to be born."* She founded the first center which has been extremely successful. The idea has spread like a prairie fire through Canada and more recently, throughout major cities in the United States. Few pregnant woman really want an abortion, but society, as mentioned, often forces them to make this choice. Birthright offers an alternative: encouragement to bear the baby, and help in finding the financial and medical assistance to do so. It operates as a center for distressed pregnant women, offering a sympathetic ear, counselling, appropriate aid, guidance or referral to existing agencies or professionals for help.

How is it publicized?

Its number should be listed in the phone book, and frequently advertised in the daily papers so that it becomes a known service. For example, in Cincinnati, its number is Ah-1-LIFE (241-5433).

Does it work?

In the first two years of the Toronto service, Birthright assisted 2,500 girls. Only a few of them chose abortion.

What age women have come to Birthright?

Most have been single and between the ages of 16 and 25. However, women of all reproductive ages have been helped.

Is Birthright connected to any church?

No. It is a private organization. It should be completely non-sectarian, and independent.

Will a girl's parents be told, if she is a minor?

She is encouraged and offered help to do so, but her wishes in the matter will be respected.

Are records kept that could later reveal secrets?

No records are kept of any kind. She need not even give her right name. It is an entirely confidential service whose only purpose is to help the woman in distress.

What if the woman is without funds?

Birthright will help her find the assistance she needs. This may include temporary employment, a home for her to live in, medical care, etc.

Is she advised to keep her baby or place it for adoption?

The decision is hers. Adoption help will be available if that is her choice.

What if she wants to keep the baby?

Approximately one-third of the girls helped by Birthright have kept their babies. When this happens, the volunteer woman who has been helping the distressed pregnant woman will help her in any way needed, even obtaining baby clothes, crib, etc.

What if she needs counseling?

Medical, religious, economic or psychological help will be available if she needs it.

Who are the ladies who staff the Birthright phone and help these women?

They are all volunteers, usually married women, but not necessarily; well-balanced, stable, concerned ladies who want to help other women.

But what of the "Clergymen's Counseling Service" or similar groups? Don't they serve the same purpose?

The question to ask about any group in your city is, "What percent of woman who are counseled ultimately have abortions?" If the number is high, recognize it for the pro-abortion group that it is.

Such a group, while claiming to be open in its advice, nevertheless often is little more than a referral service to abortionists. Some even offer financial assistance to obtain an abortion. While not insisting, they often, in effect, offer the mother little alternative to abortion.

Why did Mrs. Louise Summerhill start this organization?

Let's let her speak for herself:

"Very few women want to destroy their babies if they see a way out, but our society gives a woman little choice but abortion or a forced marriage. Otherwise, she is socially ostracized and receives little support from the community.

"The conditions that make a child unwanted must be changed. I question the credibility of anyone who is for or against abortion unless he is working to change conditions and attitudes.

"Allowing a woman to empty her womb, particularly a teenager, treats only the symptom, not the cause. The teenager may be striking out at her parents or looking desperately for affection. Psychologists say most women get pregnant deliberately, even though they may not realize it. Such a person is likely to be a repeater. We had one teenager whose mother had arranged for her to have two abortions. She was pregnant again, and came to Birthright because she wanted to have the baby.

"To my knowledge, only one of our women has been a repeater, and she has been under psychiatric care.

"If a woman carries her baby to term, she is more likely to realize that she must take some responsibility for her sexuality, and that through sexual intercourse she may create another life."

How would we start a Birthright in our city?

Probably the best start would be to phone Mrs. Summerhill, 21 Donegal Drive, Toronto 17, Canada, and ask her advice. Be sure to obtain her book, The Story of Birthright, ($3.00) and then contact one of the existing groups in Washington, D.C., Cleveland, Chicago, Denver, Portland, Dallas, Atlanta, etc. Each month new groups are being formed. (65 groups to date)

Would there be good homes available if these mothers would give their babies up for adoption?

Most emphatically yes! With the availability of abortion in New York and some other states there has been a precipitous decline in babies available for adoptions. Many adoption agencies have stopped accepting applications from childless couples and some maternity homes are even considering closing their doors. (Wall Street Journal May 3, 1971)

It looks as though babies for adoption will become almost unavailable if current trends continue. There are and will be far more good homes than babies available.

What about bi-racial babies and those from minority groups?

Many good homes, willing to adopt these babies are presently unable to do so because of lack of finances. To remedy this, seven states have made available various financial aid to qualified parents so that they can better be able to adopt and adequately care for these babies.

21

RIGHT TO LIFE

Right to Life organizations have been and are being formed in many areas. Primarily educational groups, their urgent goal is to bring the pro-life facts, such as are found in this book, to the attention of millions of Americans. Many other groups are working for similar goals such as: United for Life (San Francisco), Minnesota Citizens Concerned for Life, Voice for the Unborn (Seattle), Women Concerned for the Unborn (Pittsburgh), The Value of Life Committee (New England), and dozens of others.

Aren't these groups being formed only to fight permissive abortion laws?

Primarily they are educational, but flowing from the dissemination of this information should and will come increased opposition to the passage of such laws.

Are they only concerned about abortion?

Definitely not. While this is their major thrust at present, they are concerned about the right of humans to live at any stage of life. They are deeply concerned about the slow erosion of the right of any person to live, whether unborn or born. Infanticide, euthanasia, and other anti-life philosophies are also of great concern to such groups.

Are these groups doing anything to solve the social problems that might lead a woman to an abortion?

They certainly should be and in our experience most of their members have been involved in a wide variety of other volunteer community activities.

Aren't these organizations mostly front organizations for religious bodies?

The major organizations that we have been familiar with are not related to any specific religious organizations, and certainly are not fronts. Much of the initial activity has frequently come from church affiliated people with a deep conviction that all human life deserves respect.

One such organization I know is against flouridation, sex education in school, birth control, sterilization, and abortion. Are you asking us to support groups like this?

You may if you wish, but your authors certainly would not work with them or support them in this multiplicity of efforts. All of the things you mentioned have their strong supporters and opponents, and each can and should be considered as an individual concern. Under no circumstances, however, should Right to Life groups diversify their efforts by supporting or opposing movements that do not directly relate to the value of every human life, such as abortion, euthanasia, or infanticide. If an organization dilutes its efforts as mentioned, it will find very few people who will support all of its goals, will probably find that the great majority of people will oppose them, and the group will end up being quite ineffective. Concentrate at this time on the unborn baby's right to life if you hope to be effective.

Is there a national organization coordinating this effort?

There is an effective and hard-working national Right to Life Committee. Its address is P.O. Box 9365, Washington, D.C., 20005.

22

THE WORDS WE USE

"Reform" of abortion laws? Would the denial of the right of the unborn to live truly be a "reform"? To use the word "reform" is to agree with the pro-abortionists that present laws protecting the unborn child should be changed. It is important in this debate to consistently use words that accurately and incisively describe the truths of which we speak. Let's make words work for us, not against us. Let's remove the camouflage and show "repeal" or ' updating" of abortion laws for what it is and speak of "permissive laws", "abolishment of all controls", "denial of the unborn child's right to life" or whatever is applicable.

"Product of conception", "fetal tissue", "glob of protoplasm", "prospectus" and other high sounding phrases are all direct denials of the humanity of the growing child. Make up your mind. If you are convinced that this is a human life, call it such. Then consistently speak of "he" or "she", not "it", and speak of the ' unborn", "pre-born", or "developing child" or "baby".

"Termination of pregnancy", "interruption of pregnancy", "retroactive conception" are all verbal gymnastics behind which to hide. "Induced abortion" is more accurate. "Killing the life within the mother", "killing the fetus", or most to the point, "killing the unborn baby" directly face the issue, and therefore are the most honorable and preferable terms to use.

"Medical murder" implies a judgment of the abortionist's knowledge of the humanity of the unborn child, and willful killing. This may not be true. We would suggest that the simple phrase of "killing" of the pre-born child cannot be challenged, is not judgmental, and directly states what is being done.

"Pre-natal euthanasia" is entirely accurate when describing killing of an unborn child because he is defective. Euthanasia (mercy killing) is killing an adult because he is or has become incompetent or defective. This can also apply to children in which case it is commonly called infanticide.

Do not accept the negative label of being "anti-abortion." Rather, always speak of this movement and philosophy as being "pro-life."

When referring to those who want abortion-on-demand, speak of "abortionists' , of the "abortionist mentality", or of the "anti-life movement." Never accuse another person of not being sincere but do insist on accurate terms.

23

INSURANCE — HOSPITALS

In past years, therapeutic abortions were relatively rare and were usually done for legitimate medical reasons. Insurance policies, which included maternity benefits, usually included coverage for such abortions. Not often true for the unmarried, the practice was established that benefits were paid to the married woman.

Now that huge numbers of abortions are being done in some states, previously set patterns of insurance payments are necessitating payment for many of these.

The obvious injustice of having many policy holders unwillingly help to pay for abortions (which to them may be totally repugnant) has aroused deep resentment.

Give an example.

The Allstate Group Health Plan for Employees provides coverage for legal abortions up to a maximum of $175.00. (this company owned by Sears, Roebuck & Co.)

How about Medical Malpractice Insurance?

Even though only a small percentage of doctors actually will do abortions, all doctors under present policies would be sharing the added expense of increased malpractice insurance costs, which are passed on to patients in the form of higher fees. Quoting Mr. Frank Appleton, New York State Malpractice Insurance Indemnity representative: *"For insurance purposes, abortion should be considered major surgery."*

Are any other surgical procedures now excluded from insurance coverage?

Yes. Certain plastic surgery and other surgery on normal organs done for non-medical reasons is usually not covered. Abortion kills and removes a normal baby from a normal uterus in a normal woman for a non-medical reason and yet is now often covered!

What do you suggest?

Might we suggest, in the event of a tide of permissiveness of abortion-on-demand, that entirely new and separate hospital and medical insurance policies, excluding abortion, be made available. Rates for insurance policies totally excluding abortions, should be appreciably lower than for policies that would be carrying the load of paying for abortions.

What of the effect of increased numbers of abortions on hospital patient loads?

Estimates of the number of induced abortions that will occur if laws permit them in our country range upwards from one million. The strain that this would put on our medical facilities would be unbelieveable. It would quite simply result in an increasing and certainly at times fatal delay of admissions for people with serious medical problems. This has happened in England and in other countries where waiting lists for certain types of routine surgery have stretched beyond months and actually into years because of crowded hospitals, partly due to the urgency of the demand for abortions. (See p. 112)

24

RESOURCES

If you are interested in doing something to preserve a pro-life philosophy and practice in our country, we would suggest the following among many available as being sources of information for you. We are not listing them in any particular order of importance.

THE NATIONAL RIGHT TO LIFE COMMITTEE, Box 9365, Washington, D.C., 20005.

Offers national coordination and a large amount of factual material, leaflets, books, legal information, etc. For $5.00 they will send you a rich packet of information.

MINESOTA CITIZENS CONCERNED FOR LIFE, 4804 Nicolet Avenue, Minneapolis, Minn. 55409.

Has available a large number of sheets of invaluable information. Send them $3.00 and ask for these information sheets. They have been one of the most active pro-life groups in the United States.

IN DEFENSE OF LIFE, by Valery Dillon, of the New Jersey Right to Life Committee, Family Life Bureau, P. O. Box 399, East Brunswick, New Jersey, 08816, $4.00.

This is a looseleaf handbook, a very comprehensive and valuable one containing many reprints of important papers, reports of legislative activity and testimony, outlines of talks for physician, attorney, woman, etc., sample newsletters, directory of Right to Life groups in the United States, etc.

THE MORALITY OF ABORTION: LEGAL AND HISTORICAL PERSPECTIVES, edited by John Noonan, Professor of Law, University of California at Berkeley, Harvard University Press, 1970, $8.95.

Excellent, logical, historically accurate, well-balanced, and well worth its price. Chapters by major Protestant and Catholic theologians, historical and legal experts. You should read this if you are going to be active in the pro-life movement.

THE TERRIBLE CHOICE: THE ABORTION DILEMMA, Bantam Books, 95¢.

The report of the First International Conference on Abortion, Washington, D.C., 1967. A resource book.

LET US BE BORN: THE INHUMANITY OF ABORTION, Joyce & Joyce, Fran. Herald Press, $1.95.

A 95-page pocketbook full of well-reasoned information.

LIFE BEFORE BIRTH, Reprint, Science #27, 35¢ each, minimum order 15 copies, Box 834, Radio City Post Office, New York, 10019. Also available in filmstrips.

LOVE FOR LIFE, Durr and Maeder, Right to Life League of Southern California, 1709 W. 8th St., Los Angeles, $1.50.

A refreshing, valuable book for use in high school.

25

LETTERS

Ultimately the abortion issue will be decided by the elected representatives of the people. They should know what your thinking is on this subject.

"All that is needed for evil to triumph is for good men and women to do nothing."

Your primary task is to educate those around you to the facts contained in this book.

An equally important task is to write your views to your State Representative, State Senator and to your Governor. Write also to your National Congressman, Senators and to the President. Ask political candidates how they would vote on this issue and cast your ballots accordingly.

--- Address your letters to:

> The Hon.
> Statehouse
> Capitol of your state

--- Be brief and polite but direct.

--- Include your name and address.

--- Do this now! Then get ten other good people to do the same.

SEX
...should we wait?

by DR. and MRS. J.C. WILLKE

TEACHERS — PARENTS

It is your duty to assist young people to make this decision in a way that will help them to find happy stable marriages and also insure the integrity and stability of family life in our society in years ahead.

In this live recording, Dr. and Mrs. Willke first ask their young audience for all of the natural (non-moral, non-religious) reasons in favor of, and then opposed to, intimate sex before marriage. The frank and honest feed-back teaches us all something.

Then the reasons given are taken one by one and discussed from a medical, psychological, and sociological viewpoint. Simple but profound, the Willke's approach is thoroughly professional, easily understood, and warmly reflective of their own happy marriage.

We believe this will become an essential part of most senior high and college level consideration of the subject of pre-marital sex, as well as being indispensable in helping parents and teachers understand and help their children.

		SCHOOL EDITION (Includes Teaching Manual)
L. P. Records, 4 sides, 12", 33⅓	7.95	9.50
Cassette Cartridges, 4 sides	9.95	11.50
Tape Reels, 5", 3¾, 4 sides	10.95	12.50

At your book store or order direct, include 30¢ postage per unit.

HILTZ PUBLISHING CO.

6304 Hamilton Avenue · Cincinnati, Ohio 45224 · Phone 681-7559

(513) 681-7559

SEX EDUCATION — The How-To For Teachers

For teachers, parents, and professionals, a guide book on how sexuality is really taught, how to (and how not to) set up a school program and how to teach controversial subjects.
—See details on preceding page.

SEX, Should We Wait —

A live recording of a dialogue between Dr. and Mrs. J. C. Willke and 500 young people on the subject of sex before marriage.
—See details on preceding page.

The Wonder of Sex

The Wonder of Sex is being recommended as "basic reading" for parents and teachers of school districts educating over five million children.
—See details on preceding page.

The Wonder of Sex Records

A recording of an evening on sex education of children as given by Dr. and Mrs. Willke. See details on preceding page.

Pointers for Parents .... $ .30

Practical Guidelines for Sixth to Twelfth Graders.

HANDBOOK ON ABORTION

Single Copies	$ .95
10 or more	.85
100 or more	.75

Plus postage and handling. Bulk discounts on request.

at your book store

or

order direct

HILTZ PUBLISHING CO.

6304 Hamilton Avenue · Cincinnati, Ohio 45224 · Phone 681-7559